KING GEORGE III LEAVING WINDSOR CASTLE

FARM STOCK OF OLD

BY

SIR WALTER GILBEY, Bart.

———

THE SPUR PUBLICATIONS COMPANY
Liss, Hampshire, GU33 7PU

THE SIR WALTER GILBEY SERIES

HAY CARTING, 1795

From the picture by George Stubbs, R.A., in the Elsenham Collection

PREFACE

Railways have brought about extraordinary changes in every department of agriculture and industry.

The application of steam to land and sea transport, to factories, mines and tillage, the application of electricity to countless different purposes, and the invention and perfection of labour-saving machinery have completely revolutionised the conditions of life.

I have endeavoured to deal with one small, but important, field which has witnessed vast changes—namely, the Live Stock of the Farm.

Who can conjecture what changes, and how far-reaching, our descendants may have to record between 1901 and 2000 A.D.?

Elsenham Hall, Essex
March, 1910

IBSN 0 904558 15 0

Originally published in
1910 as *FARM STOCK 100
YEARS AGO*

Printed and bound in Great Britain by
Redwood Burn Limited, Trowbridge & Esher
Published by
THE SPUR PUBLICATIONS COMPANY
Hill Brow, Liss, Hampshire, GU33 7PU

INDEX

CONTENTS

CONTENTS

CONTENTS

CATTLE—*continued*

HORSES

CONTENTS

POULTRY—*continued*

APPENDIX

Famous agriculturists

ILLUSTRATIONS

NOTES FOR GUIDANCE (THIS EDITION)

This book was orginally published in 1910; accordingly in the text:

(a) "100 years ago" means around 1810;

(b) the "present time" refers to the period immediately prior to 1910.

FARM STOCK OF OLD

THE period with which I deal in the following pages was one of exceptional importance in the history of British Agriculture ; it was a time of change and progress.

The great possibilities that lay in careful and judicious cross-breeding had been demonstrated by such men as Robert Bakewell* and his pupil George Culley,* whose success in improving our sheep, cattle and horses was widely recognised, and may be said to have founded the new school of stock-breeding.

New methods of feeding had been introduced and prominent agriculturalists of the day—the Duke of Bedford,* the Earl of Egremont,* Sir John Sinclair* and Mr. Thomas Coke, afterwards created Earl of Leicester,* among them—took the lead in conducting experiments on a considerable

---

* *See* Appendix

I

scale to ascertain the results which could
be obtained by different methods of dieting
sheep and cattle.

THE DAWN OF VETERINARY SURGERY

The time was remarkable for another
development. The year 1791 saw the
establishment of the Veterinary College
with the famous French veterinary surgeon
St. Bel as its first Professor, and the establishment of this institution marked the
dawn of a new era in the healing art as
applied to domestic animals.

It would be too much to maintain that
there was no such thing as the treatment of
sick animals before this time ; indeed, the
necessity for teaching wiser and better
methods had been recognised twenty-five
years earlier.

Edward Snape, an eminent veterinary
surgeon, as we learn from an advertisement in Heber's *Historical List of Horse
Matches Run*, proposed to establish by
subscription "An Hippiatric Infirmary" in
1766. It does not appear, however, that
his scheme was carried into effect. Snape's
proposal was made too soon. "Farriers"
of his day knew nothing of surgery as we

3

understand the word, and their ideas on the
subject of drugs had made slender advance
upon the knowledge of two hundred years
earlier.

Bleeding—the stock remedy for equine
ills of every kind—was still practised, and
continued to be so until comparatively recent
times. The Essex farmers used to bleed
their animals regularly in spring and autumn
as late as the year 1835, and I remember
that many farmers in the district of
Elsenham continued the practice until
about 1850.

Such drastic operations as trepanning *
for glanders, however, were falling into
discredit among some practitioners.

Ideas concerning the appearance of the
horse which had held sway for hundreds of
years were also changing.

Cropping the ears, which had been
commonly practised for hundreds of years,
was going out of fashion. Blaine,† writing
in 1816, says that at this date it was " nearly
abolished."

---

* Edward Snape (*Tracts on Farriery, 1791-8*)
describes this operation, candidly adding that though
he had often performed it himself he had never known
it succeed, either in his own practice or that of others.

† D. P. Blaine *Outlines of the Veterinary Art* (*1816*)

" Nicking " was an operation whereby the horse with a drooping tail was made to elevate it in an upward curve. To give the approved carriage and shape of the tail, three incisions were made across the under part of the dock, and mechanical means were applied after the operation to prevent the severed muscles from reuniting. This operation was going out of fashion, but we gather from Blaine that it was still practised occasionally in 1816, in a less severe form.

If veterinary surgery was only in its infancy as regards equine maladies, the science did not embrace the study of cattle and sheep diseases at all. Treatment of sick cattle was referred to the local " leech," * who, to quote a writer of the time, " knows as much of the diseases of animals as the beast to which he is sent for."

It was indeed curious that during a period when energy, intelligence and wealth were successfully striving to improve the breeds of sheep and cattle, the treatment of these in illness was left to a class of men who were totally ignorant of the first principles of medicine.

---

* The animal doctor at this time was called a " leech " ; in earlier days all practitioners of medicine were so called.

AGRICULTURAL SOCIETIES

A brief sketch of the early Agricultural
Societies may be given here. The first to be
established was the " Society of Improvers "
in Scotland, which came into existence in
1723. The Dublin Society was founded in
1749. In England the Bath and West of
England Society for the Encouragement of
Agriculture, Arts, Manufactures and Commerce, was established in 1777. The
Odiham Society, whose aim was to foster
agriculture and home industries, was founded
in 1785.

The creation (due largely to the exertions
of King George III*), in 1793, of the old
Board of Agriculture, with an income from the
public purse of £3,000, was, in some measure,
instrumental in promoting the establishment
of many Agricultural Societies. Sir John
Sinclair, a very prominent agriculturalist,
was the first President, and the famous
Arthur Young† the Secretary. The Board
did not accomplish all that was expected of
it, and came to an end in the year 1822.

During the ten years after the Board
of Agriculture had been created, the

---

* *See* Appendix, p. 136
† *See* Appendix, p. 148

6

establishment and work of local Societies occupied a great deal of attention.

Some of these, as the Northumberland Society, adopted as their main object an experimental farm; many made the allotment of premiums or prizes for the best stock their principal purpose; some were founded with the definite object of making experiments of various kinds; and others aimed at the collection and circulation of useful information relating to agricultural affairs.

In 1803 there were at least thirty-two Societies for the advancement of the agricultural interest in operation throughout England and Scotland. Some of these have long ceased to exist; but others, under their original or different names, continue the work they were established to conduct in such form as the altered conditions of the industry indicate as most beneficial to those concerned.

AGRICULTURAL SHOWS

The idea of holding the Shows which, at the present time, are so conspicuous a feature of agricultural life took shape during the last years of the eighteenth century.

In 1797 was held the first Agricultural Show; it was that of the Bath and West of England Society.

Lord Somerville,* as Chairman, named the Duke of Bedford, Mr. Mighill of Wilts, Mr. Stone and Mr. Astley of Leicestershire, and Mr. Billingsley, a Vice-President of the Society, as Judges; and these, after examining the animals shown, decided that three sheep, New Leicester, belonging to Mr. Crook of Tetherton, were entitled to the prize of plate worth ten guineas.

A cow was shown, but, having been fed with meal for three weeks, was rejected.

Some North Devon cattle and others also, but the advertisement required sire, dam and offspring to be exhibited, and these not being produced, it was decided that the claimant was not entitled to the premium.

A dead New Leicester sheep was also shown; the live weight was 218 lbs.; dead the quarters weighed 160 lbs.; the carcase, being cut up, was exhibited next day in the market, and its thickness of fat much admired.

This meeting of the Bath and West of England Society in 1797 was more numerously attended than any previous gathering. Several of the nobility and some 200 farmers from various parts of the Kingdom were present.

---

* *See* Appendix, p. 152

In 1798 the Sussex Agricultural Society held its first Show at Lewes. The prize, or premium, list was practical and offered an example to be followed:—

Twenty guineas * were offered for the best 3-year-old bull, if the winning bull remain in the owner's possession for a year, to serve, for £1 1s. each, 20 cows belonging to subscribers to the Society.

Ten guineas * for the second 3-year-old bull, conditions as for the best, the service fee being 10s. 6d. only.

Ten guineas for the best 3-year-old heifer, dam of a living calf and in milk at time of Show.

Twenty guineas for the best South Down ram, one year old last lambing time. If the winning ram remain in the owner's possession, to serve 40 ewes at 10s. 6d. in October.

Fifteen guineas for the second South Down ram (service fee 7s. 6d.), ten guineas to the third ram (5s. fee), and five guineas to the fourth (2s. 6d. fee), conditions as for the first.

Ten guineas to the best South Down ewe, one year old last lambing time, and five guineas to the second.

---

* Plate to the value of each premium might be chosen by the winner in lieu of cash.

Five guineas to the best South Down wether, two years old; the three best wethers shown to be slaughtered immediately, their live and dead weight taken, and shape, fatness, and lightness of offal taken into account; loose fat not to be included in the offal.

The ewes shown were to have been kept with the flock sheep until within three days of the Show, and the fleece of each competitor was to be shown for the guidance of the judges in determining the weight and quality of the wool.

Any person might show as many cattle and sheep as he pleased, but could not take more than one prize for each.

In 1799 the "Smithfield Cattle and Sheep Society," as the Club was then called, held its first Exhibition in Smithfield; fat stock were shown at this meeting.

The schedule of prizes for the Show of 1803 included classes for :—

(a) Beasts fed on any kind of food except corn.

(b) Beasts fed without cake or corn, of 100 stone or over.

(c) The same under 100 stone.

In 1801 Lord Somerville held the first of his Shows in London. This was a notable

institution for several years; it took place in
the spring and was always well supported.
His Lordship gave substantial prizes for
draught oxen, store beasts and for sheep.

The occasional Shows held about this
time give evidence of the increased interest
being taken in the improvement of live-stock.

The roads over the greater part of the
country were still indifferent, and con-
sequently stock was sent to Shows only
from within a limited distance. Some few
animals, it is true, were sent from distant parts
of the Kingdom to the Shows held in London.

When facilities existed for doing so, animals
for exhibition were sent to London by
canal-boat. The first man to adopt this plan
is said to have been Mr. Westcar, a famous
breeder of Herefords, who thus sent an ox
weighing 241 stone to the Smithfield Show
of 1801.

Breeders would take more trouble to
send beasts a long distance to Shows in
London, because the animals went from the
Show ring to Smithfield Market to be sold.

SHEEP-SHEARING FESTIVALS

Between 1790 and 1825 the Sheep-Shearing
festivals held by great landowners gained
national importance.

EARL OF LEICESTER, Farmer and Politician (1752–1842)

For a very long period the occasion of washing and shearing the sheep on the farm had been a season of festivity, the men employed being regaled at the farmer's expense.

Mr. Coke, of Holkham, afterwards Earl of Leicester,* raised the Sheep-Shearing festivals to the proportions of a public function. "Coke's Clippings," as they were called, were begun in 1778, and twenty years later they had attained to European fame.

The Duke of Bedford† had identified himself with every movement for the improvement of stock and agriculture generally. He held his first Sheep-Shearing meeting on a large scale in 1797 ; it was so successful that when the Sheep-Shearing of 1800 was held many who wished to attend could not obtain post horses from London to Woburn until after operations were begun. The Duke kept open house at Woburn Abbey for the week the Sheep-Shearing lasted and entertained between two and three hundred visitors.

---

* *See* Appendix, p. 147
† *See* Appendix, p. 143

These great " Sheep-Shearings " had more
of the character of the modern Agricultural
Show than the avowed " Shows " organised
by society or individual.

Prominent breeders would arrange sweep-
stakes, each showing his best beast or ram
and putting down a sum of money in support
of his conviction that it should prove the
best ; thus, in 1800, at Woburn, the Duke of
Bedford, Lord Winchelsea, Lord Somerville*
and Mr. Bouverie each staked five guineas
that he would show the best Devon heifer.

The letting of rams for the ensuing season,
the exhibition of rams for prizes, and the
sale of ewes were features of the occasion.
The Duke of Bedford for several years gave
a prize of fifty guineas to the flock owner
who, during the preceding year, had spent
most money in buying Leicester or South
Down stock.

If a farmer had a remarkably fat beast,
he would show it at these Sheep-Shearing
festivals ; any novelty in the shape of
implements would be on view ; there were,
as now, competitions for the graziers and
butchers, who were invited to guess the
weight of beast or sheep, the animal being

---

* *See* Appendix, p. 152

slaughtered and cut up to ascertain whose estimate was nearest the actual weight.

As the famous Sheep-Shearings were those promoted by the great agricultural leaders of the time, the visitors were sure of seeing the best stock and the most recent appliances.

PLOUGHING MATCHES

Ploughing matches, in which were tested the merits of rival teams and often of different makes of plough, were very frequent at this time and attracted much attention.

Sometimes these matches were organised on a large scale. Thus, on 26th May, 1803, under the auspices of the Essex Agricultural Society, at Chelmsford, no fewer than 17 swing ploughs, each drawn by a pair of horses, three ploughs drawn by a yoke of oxen, and one Norfolk wheel plough entered for competition.

Each ploughman was required to do three-fifths of an acre in dry, friable, sandy loam. The prize was won by the Norfolk wheel plough, which performed the task in 1 hour $28\frac{1}{2}$ minutes; the second, a swing plough, occupying 29 minutes longer. Such competitions were very usual also at the great Sheep-Shearings.

Private ploughing matches were often arranged, a bet depending on the result. On one occasion plough teams belonging to King George III* and Lord Somerville competed against one another at Windsor.

The popularity of these competitions among our grandfathers is worthy of remark, if only because similar events are much in vogue at the present day, particularly in my own county of Essex.

Ploughing competitions, among others, have been for some years past promoted by the Education Department of the County Councils in Essex and Hertfordshire. The usual method is to require each competitor to plough half an acre with a pair of horses abreast without a driver, four hours being allowed for the task, the prizes being awarded to those who have performed it in the best and most workmanlike manner. The competition is divided into half-a-dozen classes, men over twenty being eligible for some, others being open to youths under that age ; different makes of plough are used in different classes.

These competitions are open to men who have attended at least two of the lectures given by experts engaged by the Education Department. I am informed that the success of this movement has been remarkable up

---

* *See* Appendix, p. 136

to the present time, thanks to the popularity
of the lecturer, Mr. Palmer. Formerly it
was difficult to persuade the men to attend
the lectures at all, a dozen being the largest
number. In 1908 no fewer than 147 men
attended these lectures.

MARKETS AND FAIRS

The mass of farmers and live-stock breeders
saw representative animals only at the weekly
market held in the county town or elsewhere,
and at the fairs, which latter then held a far
more important place in agricultural economy
than they do now.

The markets and most of the annual fairs
were more or less local in their influence, but
some of the fairs held very different standing.

Such, for example, was Ipswich Lamb Fair,
where as many as 120,000 lambs were collected
in good years. At the fair of 1799 the
number did not exceed 40,000, and the
deficiency was attributed to the immense
losses sustained by the flock-masters from
the extreme severity of the winter, spring

and early part of what might have been summer.*

Weyhill, in Hampshire, and the fair held on Salisbury Plain were among the most famous sheep fairs. St. Faiths, near Norwich, Market Harborough and Carlisle were famous fairs for cattle. Howden, Horncastle, Woodbridge, Pancras, in Staffordshire, and St. Faiths were great horse fairs to which further reference may be made.

The largest fair in the United Kingdom was Falkirk Tryst.† The gathering of cattle of all Scottish breeds, sheep and horses was enormous. The October Tryst was the last of the annual series of three, the others being held in August and September. As many as 50,000 cattle, 30,000 sheep and 3,000 horses might be assembled at Falkirk, whose central position (it is 22 miles from Edinburgh and 24 from Glasgow) made it the most convenient place for Scottish breeders.

The Earl of Egremont, about 1790-1800, had given the Petworth Fair something of the character of a Show. He presented

---

* *Annals of Agriculture* (Vol. 33)

† "Tryst": Scotch term for a meeting-place or market.

prizes to those who produced the best bulls
and heifers for sale.

TRAVELLING " JOBBERS "

While many different breeds of sheep
and cattle were recognised, there existed a
constant process of cross-breeding on a
small scale all over the country.

The majority of farmers travelled but little,
but they required new blood from time to
time to maintain the standard of their herds
and flocks ; and, as it was not convenient to
range the country in search of it, they
entrusted their orders to the " jobbers."

The jobbers were experts who continually
travelled, receiving and executing orders for
stock, and fulfilled a very important function
in the days when there were no railways.

The individual jobber, who confined himself
to one district, which might embrace three or
four adjacent counties wherein he had worked
up a connection, was known to and depended
on by the farmers.

In the West of England and borders
of Wales, there were cattle jobbers who
traded, for the most part, in Welsh cattle ;
in the South of England, sheep jobbers went
their rounds among the farmers of Dorset,

2

Wilts and Hampshire—counties famed for their flocks from very early times.

TITHES AND THEIR INIQUITY

" For lamb, pig and calf, and for other the like
  Tithe so as thy cattle the Lord do not strike."

Thus wrote Thomas Tusser * more than two hundred years before the period with which I deal. His lines enjoin the farmer to be honest in the matter of tithing, lest Divine judgment visit wrong-doing on his flocks and herds.

The matter of tithes does not, perhaps, come strictly within the scope of my subject; but, inasmuch as tithes were an ever-present source of trouble to the stock-breeder in the days before Commutation was adopted (1837), brief reference may be made to them.

The natural increase of farm stock, like everything else from corn to eggs, was tithable; and where tithe-owner and farmer did not agree for payment in cash, as the alternative to payment in kind, difficulties were frequent.

---

* Thomas Tusser; born at Witham, Essex, 1524; died in 1580. He was educated at St. Paul's School, and afterwards at Eton and Cambridge. These lines occur in his *January's Husbandry* (1573)

The tithe-owner was entitled to every tenth lamb produced. If the lamb crop was under fifty, the system adopted was to assemble the lambs and divide them. The farmer chose two lambs, then the tithe-owner took one; the farmer next selecting seven, then the tithe-owner chose one more; the farmer then chose nine, and the two parties took one and nine in turn until the whole tithe had been allotted.

If the lambs exceeded fifty the process was different. The lambs were collected near a gap in some hedge and driven slowly through it; the first two to pass into the adjoining field belonged to the farmer, the third to the tithe-owner, the next seven to the farmer, and thereafter each tenth lamb to pass through was the tithe lamb.

In many parishes a cash payment of a penny or three halfpence per head of the lamb crop was made instead. In one eastern county parish custom required the farmers to bring their tithe of lambs to the churchyard on St. Mark's Day, and there tie them up for the rector to remove at his convenience.

It was very usual to make some arrangement to pay tithe on calves in money, butter or cheese. The majority of farmers in any given parish would probably not possess a herd large enough to produce as many as ten calves in the season, and some other method of payment was almost a necessity; sometimes the tithe-owner was content to wait till the next year for his tenth calf.

The milk tithe was a fruitful source of trouble. The tithe-owner was entitled to a tenth of the milk given by the cows of each parishioner, but the method of paying this particular tithe varied in different parts of the country.

In some parishes local custom prescribed that every tenth quart of the total yield of the herd was the tithe; in others every tenth day's milking was the tithe; in yet others the tenth milking (cows being milked twice a day); and in other parishes, again, it was the custom to set apart the milk of the tenth cow. The law laid down that the proper tithe was a tenth of the yield of the whole herd; but this was qualified by allowances for "local customs," and these differed, as I have shown above.

Another source of difficulty arose in connection with conveyance of the tithe milk to the rector's door. The general rule was for the farmer to milk his cows into his own pails, the rector sending his own messenger with pails to receive it; but in some parishes the farmer took the milk in his own pails to the rectory, deducting an agreed quantity for his trouble.

Yet another cause of dispute over milk tithes was the question whether it was payable to the rector in whose parish the cows were pastured or to the rector in whose parish stood the house where the cows were milked. Such a difficulty, of course, would arise only in the case of a farm which lay partly in one parish and partly in another. It was eventually decided by the law courts that the tithe belonged to the rector in whose parish the cows were milked.

One striking instance of the trouble and bad feeling to which milk tithes gave rise may be mentioned. In a certain parish whose rector was not on good terms with the people, the farmers combined and tried to compel the rector to take all his tithe milk on the same day of the week. There were 400 cows in the parish, and the result was to give the unfortunate rector perhaps 250 gallons of milk on that one day and none at all on the other six. This method of paying milk tithe was ruled illegal.

As regards colts, it was very usual to accept eightpence on each animal foaled.

Swine enjoyed exemption from tithe if the litter consisted of six or less. This plan favouring the farmer, custom adjusted it by giving the tithe-owner one sucking-pig out of any litter which numbered seven or more.

Poultry paid tithe of eggs, and, as a matter of convenience, the farmer generally gave the tithe-owner annually an agreed number of eggs for each hen in his possession. A common method of compromise, and a very old one, was to give thirty eggs in Lent—a practice which we may conjecture had its origin in the pre-Reformation days, when the clergy, who were usually the tithe-owners, eschewed meat during that season.

The tithing or tithe barn—the " hated tithe barn," as a modern author who remembers the heart-burnings and quarrels of old days describes it—was a feature of the out-buildings of every large farm. Many of these barns are still in existence all over the country; they are relics of a later period when the crops were carried and tithed under cover in the barn, one portion of which was set aside for the tithe.

At this time—a hundred years ago—the practice of taking tithes in money instead of in kind was increasing. It seems to have grown out of the farmer's preference for paying these dues in cash; for we read *(Annals of Agriculture)* of the clergy threatening to revert to

TITHING BARN AT MARWELL MANOR, NEAR WINCHESTER

the old system of claiming tithes in kind if the farmers did not pay their labourers more liberally.

The wages of farm-hands is a subject which does not come within my purview. It was a matter which engaged no little attention during George III's reign (1760 to 1820), and, being closely bound up with the subject of poor-law relief, was one which greatly exercised the economists and philanthropists of the time.

RELATIVE IMPORTANCE OF STOCK

In dealing with an age in which corn-growing was the principal business of the farmer, we must always bear in mind that live-stock (save sheep) were of less account than the wheat which, protected from foreign competition by the Corn Laws, stood first in agricultural economy.

SHEEP.—Among animals the sheep was incomparably the most important, thanks to the growth of the wool industry and the demand for British woollen fabrics.

One proof of the importance attached to sheep occurs in a clause which Sir Edward Littleton (created Baron Hatherton in 1835) induced Parliament to include in an Act relating to commons. This clause forbade rams being turned on to commons after 20th August in each year, thus preventing the injury to the sheep by the use of " paltry " rams. Before this Act was passed farmers had been obliged to remove their ewes from the commons and pasture them in enclosed grounds early in September.

It is difficult for us to realise the difference between the place occupied by the sheep a hundred years ago and to-day, but the following figures may help to an understanding :—

In 1805, Mr. John Luccock *—and his estimate was generally accepted as approaching very near to accuracy—put the number of sheep in England and Wales at over 26 millions. A hundred years later—in 1901—the official returns showed under 19 millions.†

---

* Mr. John Luccock was a wool stapler of Leeds ; he wrote *The Nature and Properties of Wool*, and *An Essay on Wool ; containing an Examination of the Present Growth of Wool in every, District throughout the Kingdom, and the means pointed out for its Improvement.*

† It is not uninteresting to notice that in 1801 the population of England and Wales was something under 9 millions, while in 1901 it exceeded 32½ millions.

The great importance of the wool trade accounts for the attention paid to numbering the flocks. Its importance is further reflected in the drastic laws which forbade export.

Neither sheep nor wool might be exported from England at this time, and, as the temptation to smuggle wool over to France was very great, special laws were in force to prevent this offence in the two counties nearest the French coast—Kent and Sussex.

Every farmer (or "owner of wool"), residing within ten miles of the coast in Kent and Sussex, was required to render a written statement of the number of his fleeces to the nearest Customs officer within three days after shearing. He could not remove them from the place of shearing without a certificate, and, if he did, he forfeited the wool and a fine of 3s. per pound.

Wool might not be carried within five miles of the coast between sunset and sunrise, on pain of forfeiture, horses and conveyance being also forfeited; and, to give the general public an interest in discouraging smuggling, the Hundred in which such seizure was made was fined treble the value of the wool seized, and costs. Within fifteen miles of the coast wool could only be bought and sold under close restrictions.

Thus the Sussex and Kent farmers in the coast districts carried on their business until 1824, when these laws were repealed. They do not seem to have been entirely effective ; the profits of smuggling were high and the smugglers daring ; and the condition of affairs in the coastal districts is well shown by the fact that, if sheep strayed at night and were not quickly found, the hand of the smuggler was suspected.

Ownerless dogs appear to have been a terrible scourge in some parts of the country at this time, as·we find occasional references to them in such terms as " that curse to the sheep farmer." *

CATTLE.—Oxen stood on a footing very different from that of sheep, being of comparatively small importance. The only estimate I have found of the number of

---

* During December, 1791, and January, 1792, the mischief done by uncontrolled and mad dogs in the Bury district of Suffolk was so great that a petition urging that dogs be taxed was presented to Parliament. It was stated that 35 persons had been bitten by mad dogs, of whom eleven died.

these is offered by Arthur Young in his
Eastern Tour, written in 1770. He then
reckoned the total in England at over
2,800,000, including 684,000 draught cattle.

The fact that some 4,800,000 cattle are now
owned in England indicates the change in
the cattle-breeding industry during a hundred
years; for, in comparing Young's estimate
with modern figures, we must remember that
the use of cattle for draught is practically
unknown in our day.*

HORSES.—There are no reliable figures in
existence to show what the horse population
was at this time. In 1814, when horses
used in husbandry as well as others were
taxed, 1,204,307 in England and Wales
contributed to the Revenue. But as
single horses owned by poor persons, brood
mares, and horses used in mail, stage
and hackney coaches and post-chaises were
not liable to tax, there is wide margin for
error.

Pitt, in his Budget speech of June, 1784,
estimated the number of horses "on the
road" at 100,000; but it is not worth
going into the matter, as modern official

---

* I believe it is the case that cattle are still used for
ploughing in parts of Sussex.

returns are very incomplete, and therefore useless for comparative purposes.

The farmer was closely interested in breeding horses; and the earlier years of the last century, by reason of the improvement of roads* and the consequent increase in the number of coaches, saw the production of more horses than have ever been bred in England before or since. There was at this time an additional demand for horses caused by the French wars.

PIGS.—Swine had always been an important feature of the farmer's stock from very early times, as I have shown elsewhere,† and, at the period of which I write—a hundred years ago—much attention was being paid to the improvement of our native breeds, principally by crossing with Chinese blood.

I think it doubtful whether pigs were kept in such large numbers during George III's reign as were kept three hundred years earlier; the changes which had been brought

---

* The badness of the roads until this time is clearly proved by the large number of patents granted for devices to prevent carriages overturning.—*Early Carriages and Roads.* By Sir Walter Gilbey, Bart. (Vinton & Co., 1903)

† *Pig in Health.* By Sir Walter Gilbey, Bart. (Vinton & Co., 1907)

about in the character of the country must have compelled reduction in the great herds of swine.

When a large proportion of England was covered with forest or lay waste, pigs could be, and were, pastured in a half-wild state under the care of swine-herds. When the forests were gradually cut down and the wastes brought under cultivation and enclosed, the land could be more profitably employed, if not for corn, then for the pasturage of sheep.

Hence, while it is reasonable to suppose that fewer pigs were kept, it can be stated as a fact that those owned a hundred years ago were more carefully bred and tended ; they had become strictly domestic animals, and no longer lived the half-wild life of their ancestors.

The pig was perhaps more important to the poor man, the labourer and the cottager, than to the well-to-do farmer. Some of the great agriculturists of the day took a keen interest in the improvement of pigs, and encouraged pig-keeping among their tenants and others.

POULTRY.—Fowls were not regarded as of much importance, generally speaking.

Exception to the rule must be made in respect of those districts where special attention was devoted to the breeding of particular kinds of feathered stock ; as the Lincolnshire fens, where goose-keeping provided many persons with a livelihood, and Norfolk, where turkeys were reared in great numbers.

SHEEP

Sheep, as I have said, held the most important place among live-stock.

Great variety of breed was recognised at this period. Richard Parkinson * enumerates no fewer than thirty-seven different British breeds, including the Merino. George Culley,† of whom mention has before been made, however, says there were fourteen British varieties, remarking that the "number-less flocks that are everywhere spread over the face of this island are exceedingly intermixed and varied."

In the absence of facilities for transport to the Shows which have since enabled farmers to study different breeds conveniently, and by reason of the stay-at-home life led by our grandfathers, local breeds had been developed and, in course of time, acquired their distinguishing characteristics.

---

* *Treatise on the Breeding and Management of Live-Stock* (1810)

† *Observations on Live-Stock* (1807) *See* Appendix, p. 142

It will be of interest to know what breeds were then, and still are, recognised. The following fifteen modern breeds were known a hundred years ago :—

Dishley or New Leicester, Southdown, Lincoln, Gloucester, Dartmouth (Dartmoor) Notts,* Exmoor, Dorsetshire, Herefordshire, Ryelands, Herdwick, Cheviot Welsh, Oxford, Kent and Hampshire.

The Dishley is now called the Leicester ; the Gloucester, the Cotswold ; the Dorsetshire, the Dorset Horn; the Herefordshire, the Ryeland ; the Welsh, the Welsh Mountain ; the Oxford, the Oxford Down ; the Kent, the Kent or Romney Marsh ; and the Hampshire, the Hampshire Down.

In addition to these there were twenty breeds which modern sheep-masters have ceased to recognise, viz :—

Durham or Teeswater, Norfolk, Nottingham Forest, Dunfaced, Shetland, Pennestone, Cumberland, Westmoreland, Northumberland, Warwickshire, Hertfordshire, Berkshire, Wiltshire, Portland, Irish, Wicklow Hills, Isle of Man (two breeds), and Somersetshire (two breeds).

---

*" Nott," Not," " Knot " or " Nat" is an old term meaning hornless.

This does not exhaust the list, but it is doubtful whether such varieties as the Sutton Coldfield (Staffs) and Windsor Forest should be regarded otherwise than as strictly local varieties. They were not important either in number or merit.

Nine breeds have been evolved during the last century or were not considered worthy of notice a hundred years ago, viz :—

Suffolk, Wensleydale, Border Leicesters, Shropshire, Devon Longwool, South Devons, Lonks, Kerry Hill, and Black-faced Mountain.

Thus it appears that the progress of sheep-breeding during one hundred years has resulted in a reduction from thirty-four British breeds to twenty-three.

There existed great variety of opinion concerning the most profitable breed for any given situation, and experiments of the most elaborate kind were made by private persons and were fostered by the Agricultural Societies.

In 1801 the Bath and West Society offered a prize of twenty guineas : —

"To the Stock Farmer who shall have bred and kept . . . the greatest number and most profitable sort of sheep in proportion to the size of his farm, in consequence of

3

his having changed his flock from what had been usually kept . . . in the neighbourhood."

The prize was claimed by Mr. Jones, of Wellington, and Mr. William Dyke, of Wiltshire ; and the Committee appointed to inspect the farms of these gentlemen awarded the prize to Mr. Dyke, who had substituted South Downs for Wiltshires twelve years before. Mr. Dyke was the first Wiltshire farmer to introduce South Downs into the county, and he fed 460 of these sheep on land which had formerly carried from 320 to 360 breeding ewes of the county variety. The change produced an increased profit of £315 5s. per year.

MERINO SHEEP

It was in the year 1792 that King George III procured from Spain * the first Merinos imported direct into this country—five rams and thirty-five ewes—and these

---

* It is to be remembered that Spain, in old days—1450 to 1550—was the most prosperous country in Europe. The Spaniards possessed not only the finest sheep in the Merino, but horses and cattle, and also sporting dogs, especially the Spanish double-nosed Pointer, which was greatly prized in England. The famous artist, George Stubbs, R.A., painted a particularly fine picture of " The Spanish Pointer."

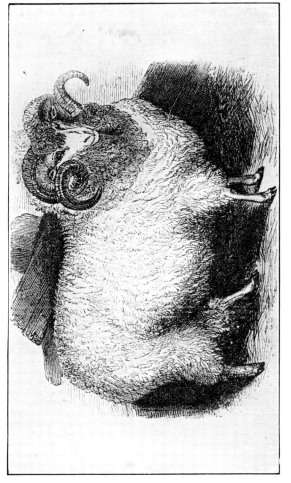

MERINO SHEEP, 1825

(*From Youatt's Book on "Sheep"*)

formed the foundation of a flock kept in the Duke of York's park at Oatlands, in Surrey.

The introduction of the Merino was an event which alone made the period 1790-1810 remarkable in the history of live-stock.

There is not now, nor has there been for very many years, a pure-bred Merino sheep in this country.

The Merino cross had been tried before George III imported Merinos direct from Spain. Merinos—so-called—had been used by Mr. Morris, of Glynde, in Sussex, and others.

Mr. Arthur Young, on one of his journeys in 1791,* saw the progeny of a half-Spanish half-Ryelands ram crossed on a South Down ewe. The Merino parent of the ram had been imported from France, and "was by no means of the true Segovian blood."

Mr. Morris informed Young that he "was getting out of the breed, from being convinced that they are not so hardy as the South Downs, not bearing equally well the sharp winds."

Other South Down breeders had tried Merino blood, procured from France and, it

---

* *Annals of Agriculture* (Vol. 17)

is to be assumed, not pure and did not persevere with it, for the same reason—the alleged inability of the cross to withstand the climate.

At Lewes Fair, in the year mentioned (1791):—

"Mr. John Ellman, of Glynd, had a ram for sale at a very low price, which nobody bought, half-Spanish and half-South-Down, weight, alive, 170 lbs. at five years old, which very much exceeded in form, wool and *feeling*, most of the rams to be seen at the fair, but nobody relished enough to use him. One proof, in a thousand others, how predominant prejudices are, and how difficult to eradicate."

When, therefore, King George III imported his flock with the object of demonstrating the superiority of Merino wool and the ability of the breed and its crosses to thrive, he had prejudice to contend against—flock-masters had already tried and condemned the Merino.

The opinion of a man who seems to have kept an open mind on the subject may be worth quoting here. In July, 1792, Mr. J. Boys, of Betshanger, a well-known

flock-master of the time, made an excursion
on horseback through a number of counties,*
and visited, among others, the Royal Farm

THE ASHFORD CUP

Won by Mr. Boys with the best South Down yearling
Ram at Ashford Wool Fair in 1809 (Now in the
Elsenham Collection)

* *Annals of Agriculture* (Vol. 19)

at Windsor, where the "Spanish flock" then was. Mr. Boys thus describes them :—

"The rams many of them much superior to Mr. Young's Don.* Their fleeces very thick and fine, the size of the carcase rather less than the South Down, but by no means so well shaped, being very narrow on the chine and thick about the throat, with large horns. If these defects could be remedied, this kind of sheep would certainly be an acquisition to this country, provided that the quality of the wool could be retained ; but will not such rich pasture as these sheep live upon soon change the quality of the wool ? "

Mr. Boys' doubts were shared by all his contemporaries save a few. Sir Joseph Banks † and Mr. Young were among the believers in the Merino, but the prevailing prejudice against the breed was not easy to break down.

In the first place, the Royal flock appeared not to thrive. The mortality among the lambs was so great that close enquiry was made. It was found that the men in charge regarded dead lambs as a perquisite. The appropriation of the skins of dead lambs

---

* A Merino ram given by the King to Arthur Young.
† *See* Appendix, p. 153

by the shepherds was forbidden and the mortality was reduced to a normal average.

The manufacturers to whom the first wool clip was shown acknowledged its excellence, but, fearing that it would "not prove in manufacture so valuable as its appearance promised," none would offer a price for it.

To prove that Merino wool did not lose its quality in the process of manufacture into cloth, it was manufactured at the King's own expense :—

"This was done year after year in various manners, the cloth always proving excellent. Yet the persons to whom the wool was offered for sale still continued to undervalue it, being prepossessed with an opinion that though it might not at first degenerate, it certainly sooner or later would alter its quality for the worse."*

In 1796 it was determined to sell the wool at any price it might fetch. Some manufacturer—encouraged, we must suppose, by the results obtained in the shape of "superfine broad cloth" made at the royal expense—bought it at 2s. per pound, which was a little more than the price ruling for

---

* *An Account of the Introduction of the Merino Sheep.* By C. P. Lasteyrie. Translated by Benjamin Thompson, 1810.

South Down wool at the time. In 1797 the
clip sold for 2s. 6d. per pound; and in 1799, the
value of the wool being now in some degree
acknowledged, the clips of 1798 and 1799,
"washed in the Spanish manner," consisting
of 89 fleeces, were separated into three lots,
according to quality, and sold respectively
at 5s., 3s. 6d. and 2s. 6d. The bulk of
the wool, 167 lbs., was of the best quality.
There were 23 lbs. of the second, and 13 lbs.
of the third quality.

These prices were regarded as extraordinary, and were accounted for—to some
extent, at least—by the fact that imported
Spanish wool was dearer in 1799 than it had
ever been known. South Down wool, at this
time, was bringing from 2s. to 3s. per pound.

The King had been giving away Merinos
to various persons who would undertake to
use them for crossing purposes, and over
one hundred rams and some ewes had thus
been distributed.

The Merino cross had now been proved
to increase the quantity and improve the
quality of fleece in every kind of short-woolled
sheep on which it had been tried, more
particularly the South Down, Hereford, and
Devonshire breeds.*

---

* *Annals of Agriculture* (Vol. 35)

In 1799, considering that the value of the breed had been established, the King ordered a number of rams and ewes to be sold to any purchaser at low prices. Five guineas was named as the medium price for a ram, and two guineas for a ewe.

Sir Joseph Banks was entrusted with the management of the business, and we may form our own opinion of the rapidity with which the value of the Merino cross became recognised from the prices paid for the Royal flock in 1809. The sale was held in Kew Gardens, forty rams and sixty ewes being offered. The former realised an average of about $46\frac{1}{2}$ guineas, two bringing 75 guineas each; the latter an average of over $32\frac{1}{2}$ guineas, one bringing 48 guineas. We may compare these figures with those paid for some ninety South Down ewes sold at the Duke of Bedford's Sheep-Shearing a month earlier; the highest price obtained was £4 16s. per head, paid for a lot of ten.

In 1810, eighteen years after the King's importation, Arthur Young was able to inform the great French authority, Lasteyrie, that there were some Merino sheep "in almost every district of Great Britain," and that they had been successfully crossed with various English breeds.

Though Merinos are not now bred in England, they are to be found in large flocks in other parts of the world where climate and pasture are suitable. They are, for instance, extensively bred in Australia and in parts of America.

Mr. J. Parker Whitney, of Whitney Bros., the great sheep breeders of California, informs me that his firm, in 1856, bought 300 of the best Merinos obtainable in Australia and shipped them by sailing vessel to San Francisco. Of the 300 shipped, only 120 head survived the passage, and these were placed on Messrs. Whitney's farm, Spring Valley Ranch, Placer County. From these, and from pure Merino rams obtained from time to time since in Vermont, U.S.A., have sprung a flock which now numbers about 20,000 head. The "Whitney Clip," for thirty years past, has been famous in the American markets.

DISHLEY OR NEW LEICESTER SHEEP

Perhaps one reason why the merits of the Merino were not more readily recognised — or, let us say, why flock-masters were not more ready to give the breed trial—was that the Dishley or New Leicester sheep at this

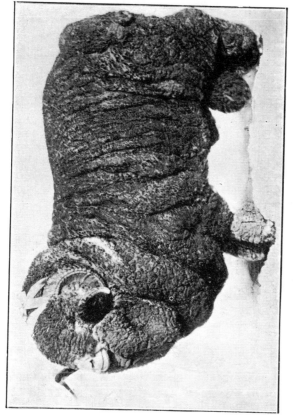

CHAMPION MERINO RAM

At New South Wales Show, 1908

time held such a conspicuous place in the eyes of the stock-breeding world.

The first marked improvement in the Leicestershire breed was accomplished, as William Marshall * tells us, by one Joseph Allom, who began life as a plough-boy and became a farmer. How he brought about the improvement in his flock does not appear to be recorded. It may be that he successfully used such Merino blood as he was able to procure; but, however it was accomplished, Allom became known for the superiority of his breed of sheep, and it grew to be the custom for farmers of standing to buy ram lambs from him. He was the only man who became distinguished as a breeder before Bakewell's time, and Marshall, reasonably enough, believed that the Leicestershire breed, through Allom's flock, had passed the first stage of improvement before Bakewell's day.

Robert Bakewell, of Dishley,† was about thirty years of age when he began to make a name for his improved breed of sheep. He preserved great secrecy about his methods of breeding. The New Leicester

---

* *Rural Economy of the Midland Counties* (2nd Edition, 1796) *See* Appendix, p. 154

† *See* Appendix, p. 139

breed, however, won renown all over the country. The Bishop of Llandaff introduced them into Westmoreland about the year 1792.

Bakewell had kept in view smallness of bone, improvement of bone, improvement of shape, fattening quality and flavour of mutton ; and his success in achieving his end was generally acknowledged. Probably the appreciation which his breed enjoyed would have been even greater had it been as remarkable for wool as for mutton.

The wool of the New Leicester was shorter than the generality of Longwools, the ordinary length of staple being from 5 to 7 inches, and it varied much in fineness and weight. So thin and light was the wool that breeders used to clothe their rams to protect them from the weather.

Were it not for this result of his experiments, we might be tempted to assume that Bakewell used Merino blood and thought it wise to keep his use of it a secret.

Despite its shortcomings as a wool-producer, the New Leicester was vastly superior to the majority of contemporary breeds, though there were flock-masters who stoutly upheld the merits of the South Down.

ROBERT BAKEWELL

(Copied, by permission of the Royal Agricultural Society of England, from the Portrait in their possession)

Culley * gives the following particulars of the two breeds :—

New Leicester, 2-year-old wether, average 20 lbs. to 30 lbs. per quarter.

,,   ,,   wool, average 8 lbs. a fleece ; sold, 1792, at 10*d.* per pound.

South Down 2-year-old wether, average 18 lbs. per quarter.

,,   ,,   wool, average $2\frac{1}{2}$ to 3 lbs. a fleece ; sold, 1792, at 2*s.* per pound.

There is no comparison between the weight of a long wool and a short fleece.

Bakewell was practically the originator of the system of ram-letting. In 1807 he was hiring out rams of his own breeding for 400 guineas a-piece for the season, and was receiving 10 guineas a service for ewes sent to the rams he kept at Dishley.

SOUTH DOWN SHEEP

The South Down was famous alike for quality of wool, excellence of mutton and for hardiness of constitution.

---

* *Observations on Live-Stock* (1807) *See* Appendix, p. 142

Mr. John Ellman, of Glynde, in Sussex, was one of the most successful breeders of South Downs at this time. He is said to have " done for the Shortwools what Bakewell did for the Longwools."

Mr. Coke, who established his Sheep-Shearing meeting in the first place as a method of bringing about improvement in the Norfolk breed, selected South Downs to replace the Norfolks on his own farm in 1792,* when the New Leicester had been long and successfully established at Holkham, and many experiments had been made.

The time was one of experiment in crossing breeds of sheep by prominent agriculturists. Those made by the Duke of Bedford at Woburn were the most note-worthy, and did much to advance knowledge of sheep-mastery.

One series of experiments, conducted in the winter of 1794-5, demonstrated the superiority of the South Down over the New Leicester in point of hardiness when kept on poor food—a matter of no small importance when we consider that a very

---

* *Annals of Agriculture* (Vol. 19) When Mr. Coke afterwards the Earl of Leicester, came to Holkham, in 1776, there were only 700 sheep in the parish. In 1791-2 he himself wintered 2,400.

considerable proportion of the flocks in England and Wales were kept on poor pasturage.

In 1801 Mr. T. Davis, of Longleat, reported that his trial of South Downs on the Wiltshire Downs (an experiment made at the instance of the Bath and West Society) had been so successful that he and his farming neighbours were replacing their flocks of the local horned breed with South Downs.

In 1801 Mr. Curwen, of Windermere, wishing to improve the mountain sheep in his district, which were very small and coarse-woolled, introduced 100 South Down ewes and two rams ; and, he was able, in 1804, to report his enterprise successful.

The advantages of the South Down over the Norfolk were perhaps best shown by a statement compiled by Sir Charles Davers, of Rushbrook Hall, Suffolk. From 1786 to 1799 he kept Norfolks, the flock averaging 610 in number. In 1800 he replaced these by South Downs, and on 80 acres less ground maintained an average of 845 head per year.

LINCOLN SHEEP

Lincolnshire, said Culley, writing in 1807, " has the same right to be called the mother county, or county for long-woolled sheep, that Lancashire has to long-horned cattle."

The Lincoln sheep at this time was large, with a long, thin and weak carcase. The 3-year-old wether weighed from 20 lbs. to 30 lbs. per quarter; it had large bones and thick, rough, white legs; the wool was from 10 to 18 inches long, and weighed from 8 lbs. to 14 lbs. per fleece. The mutton was coarse-grained, and the sheep fattened slowly on any but the rich Lincolnshire marshes.

Bakewell is stated by some to have laid the foundation of the Dishley breed with Lincoln blood. Culley, who, as a pupil of Bakewell, may have had opportunities for learning his master's secrets, says that the Lincolnshire breeders

> "suffered the same discerning set of breeders from the Midland counties to rob them of a much more valuable breed of sheep, which they undoubtedly were first in possession of, before they were suffi-ciently sensible of the value of them."

This appears to mean that Bakewell made of the Lincoln sheep a use which Lincoln-shire farmers failed to make for themselves.

The slow development of the breed was a point in its disfavour. An eminent breeder stated that few were ready for market at two-shear, and that many farmers were obliged to winter some of their three-shears before they were ready for the butcher.

This was a breed strictly confined to its native county ; it had the reputation of being unsuitable for any land other than the low-lying, rich marshes, by reason of its "very tender" character. Nor was it in any demand for crossing upon other breeds, owing to its indifferent shape and the coarseness of the mutton. Culley says, "Whatever crosses I have seen from Lincolnshire tups, in general, did harm."

The Lincolnshire breeders were slow to recognise the value of the Dishley breed, and perhaps this can be explained. Wool was the main object of the Lincoln breeders, and long heavy wool had commanded high prices up to the time of the American War (1774-1782).

The fixed belief of the Lincolnshire breeders in the superiority of their "marsh sheep" remained long after the price of wool had fallen, and only about the year of 1790 did some few of the more enterprising among them begin to try the New Leicester cross.

The cross-breds, it was found, matured earlier, and made a better quality of mutton,

4

while the yield of wool was not appreciably affected, and in the earlier years of the last century the practice of buying and hiring New Leicester rams was becoming general. So widely was the Dishley cross used in 1851, Mr. J. A. Clarke * stated, that the pure old-fashioned Lincolns were then scarcely to be found except in some few parts of the county.

COTSWOLD SHEEP

The wool trade and the wool manufactures were far more important in Gloucestershire a hundred years ago than they are now. In early times the Cotswold wool was held the finest in England.

Young, who rode through the district in 1783, says :—

" The principal object in the country is their sheep, which are good and bear longer wool than any breed I know on such poor hills. It is an exception to common rules, which seem to proportion the length of the fleece to the richness of the pasture. Their wool is six or eight inches long, in large bushy fleeces of 5 to 8 lbs., and sells at 7*d.* a pound. The

---

* *Journal of the Royal Agricultural Society* (Vol. 12, 1st Series)

sheep are about 20 lbs. a quarter, fat ;
some I heard of rise to 28 lbs."

The Cotswold breed differs from the hill
and upland breeds in other parts of the
Kingdom in that it is large and long-woolled,
whereas other hill sheep are small and short-
woolled. There is some doubt whether
New Leicester blood was used by Cotswold
flock-masters, but it is certain that the breed
was greatly improved during the period
(1790 to 1810) with which I am dealing.

DARTMOOR AND EXMOOR SHEEP

The Dartmoor and Exmoor sheep were
very much alike, the principal difference
being that the latter were a little smaller.
These breeds do not seem to have been
of much account outside their own county,
though the "Bampton Nott" or "Nat" (*i.e.*
Bampton hornless sheep) is mentioned with
approval by old writers.

The modern Devon breeds differ much
from those of a hundred years back. Like
other sheep, the Devonshire varieties shared
in the general improvement during the earlier
years of the century.

An advertisement of "two capital Leicester
Rams" at Morebath, which were offered for

service at 2 guineas a ewe in 1802, shows that the Dishley blood had found its way to this part of England.

The Devon Longwool was the result of crossing the Improved Leicester on the old Bampton Nott, a large heavy-fleeced sheep. This breed was established in the early forties.

DORSET SHEEP

This breed, now known as the "Dorset Horned," is a very old one. Mr. R. H. Rew, now Assistant-Secretary of the Board of Agriculture, in his Report on the sheep shown at Windsor in 1889,* says that these sheep have been "naturalised in their native county from time immemorial and preserved practically unmixed."

Over a large area, the Dorset has given way to the South Down. The Dorset of a hundred years ago was smaller and carried a fleece inferior to its modern descendant. It is noted for its peculiar aptitude for breeding at all seasons of the year, though modern flock-masters do not encourage this peculiarity.

* *Journal of the Royal Agricultural Society* (Vol. 25, 2nd Series)

RYELAND SHEEP

The Ryeland is a very old breed; it was a
native of the Welsh marshes and certain
sandy tracts of country south of the Wye.
Though small it was famed both for the
excellence of its mutton and the quality
of its wool.   The tracts whereon it was
bred were formerly given up to the cultivation of rye, the belief being that no other
grain could be profitably grown thereon—
whence the name of the local sheep.   It was
among the first breeds to show the advantages
of the Merino cross.

The Ryeland, by reason of its small size,
has lost favour, and few flock-masters prefer
it nowadays.   In 1863 it was said to be almost
extinct, but representatives of the breed
are still to be seen at the "Royal" every
year.

It had other merits, as Lord Somerville
bore witness in his address to the Board of
Agriculture in 1799 * :—

"Of the Ryland I can, from experience,
assert that no sheep in this Kingdom are
worth more upon an average per pound;
none will bear to stock more thickly on land,

or look starvation better in the face, provided they are protected from cold."

HERDWICK SHEEP

The hardiness of this breed constituted its value. A hundred years ago the Herdwick was in demand for crossing to improve the hardiness of other flocks in various parts of the neighbouring counties. Culley wrote, in 1807 :—

"They have no hay given to them in winter, but support themselves in the severest storms and deepest snows by scratching down to the heath or other herbage. They do not face the coming storm, as reported, but, like other sheep, turn their backs on it ; and in such weather they generally gather together and keep stirring about, by which means they tread down the snow, keep above it and are rarely overblown."

The origin of this breed is doubtful. The old writers are generally agreed that the original stock came from some other region, and are not native to the country they inhabit ; but the authorities differ one from another concerning the source whence the parent stock is derived. The most reasonable assumption is that it was originally a Welsh breed.

A hundred years ago the Herdwick was small, with a fleece 2lbs. to 2½lbs. of thick and matted short wool, coarser than that of most other short-woolled sheep, but finer than that of the black-faced Heath breed. The hairy or "kempy" quality of the wool has been much less marked during the last fifty years. They have been greatly improved, and have spread over a somewhat wider area. In 1866, when Mr. H. H. Dixon ("The Druid") described them, they covered Cumberland, Westmoreland and part of Lancashire.

CHEVIOT SHEEP

The Cheviot district and its flocks were inspected in 1791 by Sir John Sinclair and Mr. Belsches. So high was the opinion of these sheep they expressed, that the British Wool Society, with the object of encouraging farmers in the hilly parts of England and Scotland to introduce the blood, bought fifty tups and a hundred ewes, which they offered to any who would try them at the low price of 36s. a tup and 20s. a ewe.

When Culley wrote (1807), the Cheviot breed had been greatly improved by

Mr. Robson, either by the use of Dishley or Lincoln blood—the authorities are not agreed which. Whatever his method, Mr. Robson brought great judgment and discretion to bear on his work, and wrought an improvement in the breed which went far to increase its popularity and the area over which it was raised.

During the past fifty years Cheviots have gained enormously in favour, as is proved by the sales at Perth and elsewhere. They cannot now be considered a strictly mountain breed, as they are purchased to stock lower-lying lands.

WELSH SHEEP

This breed, in its purity, seems to be very much the same to-day as it was a hundred or, for that matter, 300 years ago. Cotswold, Leicester, and other sheep were introduced and banished the smaller and less profitable breed to the higher grounds, where they have remained, uncrossed, in undisputed possession of pastures where a less hardy sheep would perish, and one more dainty would rapidly deteriorate.

The Welsh breed found favour in England a hundred years ago. Mr. Conyers, of Copt

Hall, in Essex, kept them in preference
to others. Mutton and wool were both
esteemed; the wool averaged about $2\frac{1}{2}$ lbs.
per fleece and brought a comparatively high
price, making the sheep a profitable one.
Their value was considerably advanced when
raised on superior pastures.

OXFORD SHEEP

The Oxford sheep of a hundred years ago,
described as being "equal in mutton to
Lincoln and Leicester, and rather better
liked," was a widely different animal from the
modern Oxford Down. The latter was
brought into existence about 1830-1840, being
the result of endeavours to combine, in one
breed, the weight and wool of the Longwool
with the quality of the Shortwool.

The modern breed traces its descent
from various crosses. The late Mr. Charles
Howard, of Bedford, crossed the Improved
Leicester and the South Down about
1830-1840, and other breeders crossed the
Cotswold and South Down and the Hampshire and Cotswold. The breed, when
established as such, was for long known as
the " Down Cotswold."

KENT OR ROMNEY MARSH SHEEP

This breed owes less than any other in England to the New Leicester. For a long time the Kent breeders refused to use Bakewell's breed, and, when they did recognise its superiority, they gave the Romney Marsh a slight infusion, enough to secure greater fattening aptitude, and then renounced outside aid.

A note in the *Annals of Agriculture* (Vol. 32) tells us that, in 1799, some 60,000 acres were occupied by Romney Marsh sheep, which numbered 240,000 head.

At this time it was the general opinion of flock-masters that carcase, shape, and tendency to fatten had deteriorated owing to lack of care and attention in breeding. They averaged, at two-shear, 22 lbs. a quarter.

Mr. Wall, a prominent breeder of the time, who had brought about considerable improvement, killed, in 1797, a sheep which weighed 45 lbs. per quarter. He had been particularly successful in improving shape and wool, reducing bone, and procuring tendency to fatten.

Mr. Wall, in an essay contributed to the *Annals of Agriculture* about this time, refers with approval to the good results which might be obtained from the use of Dishley blood, and it is reasonable to suppose that he was one of the first to use it.

HAMPSHIRE SHEEP

The modern Hampshire Down has little more in common with the old Hampshire than the name. In 1793 Arthur Young wrote :—

> "It was for some time a question whether the Hampshire or the South Downs were the better breed ; but it seems now to be entirely decided in favour of the South Downs, which gain ground on the others everywhere, and are even beating them out of their own country, the Hampshire Hills. Hampshires are very subject to the rickets (here called the 'goggles'), a distemper never known with the South Downs."

The modern breed is descended from this cross and a cross between the South Down and Berkshire Knot or Nott.

TEESWATER SHEEP

Of the breeds no longer recognised, the Teeswater, otherwise known as the "Durham," was one of the most important, certainly in the north of England. It was the largest

English sheep. Mr. Bakewell once made an experiment to discover the quantity of turnips eaten during a fortnight by a ram of each of six breeds, and the weights of the several animals show the superior size of the Teeswater. They were :—

Teeswater, 290 lbs. ; Wiltshire, 173 lbs. ; Norfolk, 162 lbs. ; Dishley (or New Leicester), 158 lbs. ; Charnwood Forester (Leicestershire), 131 lbs. ; Herefordshire, 115 lbs.*

The Teeswater ewes were noteworthy for the high proportion of twin lambs produced ; they seldom brought forth three, but single lambs were so uncommon that the rate of increase was equal to that of more prolific breeds. It was held also the most profitable sheep, from the butcher's point of view, the mutton being considered finer than that of the Lincoln. It was not, however, among the best wool producers ; the wethers averaged 7 lbs. per fleece and the ewes about 6 lbs.

NORFOLK SHEEP

This breed, it was remarked by a writer of a century ago, would more correctly be called the " Suffolk," as the best flocks were to be

---

* *Annals of Agriculture* (Vol. 6)

found in the neighbourhood of Bury St. Edmunds.

The old Norfolk has now disappeared. It is described as being so long of leg, light of carcase, and large of bone that it more resembled a deer than a sheep. Some Norfolk and Suffolk rams had horns no less than 35 to 37 inches long, following the curves.

The Norfolk was an unprofitable variety, but local prejudice was difficult to remove.

Some reason could be assigned for the preference given the local breed by Norfolk sheep-masters.

Until measures had been taken to improve the pastures in the county a great part of it was wild, bleak and unproductive ; the grazing was so poor that only an active and hardy sheep could thrive upon it, by reason of the distances they had to travel daily in their search for a bite. Improved breeds could not thrive on such lands ; hence the disinclination of the farmers to give up the old Norfolk breed, which was so well suited to the then existing conditions of keeping.

Mr. Coke (Earl of Leicester) was among the first to undertake the task of proving to Norfolk farmers that the local breed could be improved upon ; he proved his case after he had introduced folding, marling and the bettering of pasture, and had replaced his flocks of Norfolks by South Downs, demonstrating the superiority of the latter in a practical way. The modern Suffolk is, at the present time, in high repute.

OTHER BREEDS

Of the breeds mentioned it may be observed that the Border Leicester was actually in existence a hundred years ago, but had not gained recognition outside the district where it had its origin. Mr. R. H. Rew * remarks that this is perhaps the only breed whose origin can be assigned to an absolute date—that is to say, the year 1767, in which the brothers Culley, pupils of Bakewell, went to Northumberland, taking a flock of New Leicesters with them. Whether they crossed these upon local breeds or not is unknown. Mr. John Usher thinks Cheviot blood was used to some extent ; Mr. Wood finds reason to hold that no crossing took place.

The old Shropshire or " Morse Common " sheep was the foundation stock of the modern

---

* Report on the Sheep exhibited at Windsor—*Journal of the Royal Agricultural Society*, October, 1889.

Shropshire breed. Credit for improving them is assigned to Mr. Samuel Meire, who obtained South Downs from Glynde and introduced New Leicester blood to obtain greater docility. The change was in progress about a hundred years ago.

The Wensleydales at this period were called " Mugs," and are held to have been a branch of the Teeswater breed. Some New Leicester blood was introduced at a somewhat later period. Culley regarded the sheep of this district and Craven as being probably a cross between the Cheviot and Dorset breeds.

The Dunfaced was a very small, hornless breed of excellent mutton. It was conjectured that it traced descent from, or had been crossed by, sheep introduced by the wreck of the Spanish Armada.

CATTLE

It is to be borne in mind that our grandfathers estimated the value of beasts by
standards differing from ours.

A hundred years ago the ox was still
widely used for draught and plough, but to
what extent it is impossible now to say for
certain, as the authorities differ; some
maintaining that the ox was giving place
to the horse, others affirming that horse-
draught was not gaining ground.

Reviewing the matter as we are able
to do with the assistance afforded by the
wealth of information collected at the time
by Arthur Young, William Marshall and
many others, it is clear that in some
counties — Sussex, Kent, and Devon, for
example — oxen were very generally used
for draught, while in the Midland counties
horses were preferred. In Norfolk and
Suffolk, also, horses were most generally in
use.

It depended much upon the suitability
of the local breed whether oxen were employed or not.

One thing was clear, namely, that Ox-draught *versus* Horse-draught was a standing topic of discussion during the period 1790-1810, or thereabouts, the advocates of each method urging reasons, supported by experience, in favour of their views.

Men naturally argued the question by the light of the conditions prevailing in their own district, and opinion and practice differed in various parts of England.

There was a very large and influential body of opinion which favoured the use of oxen for draught on general principles. King George III was a warm advocate of it. When Pitt, in 1801, proposed to lay an additional tax on horses, he urged, as one valuable result likely to follow the step, that it would bring about the more general use of oxen for draught purposes—a change which would promote cattle-breeding and increase the meat supplies of the country.

The demand for beef, and the discovery that it was more profitable to kill beasts when young—say from two to three years old—brought about the disuse of cattle for draught purposes. Working cattle were not killed until worn out at seven to nine years old.

5

The usual method of employing general-purpose cattle was to put them to the yoke at the age of two or three years—it varied with different breeds or with local usage—work them until seven or more, and then fatten them on the richest pasture for the butcher.

The system of ploughing by oxen is followed at the present day in many districts of France. The excellence of the "under-cut" of the joint from such beasts is beyond question; the rest of the carcase is generally boiled down to make ragouts and the soup which figures so largely on French tables.

In England, at this period, agricultural authorities, when reviewing the merits of any given breed, took into account three qualities :—

(1) Its fitness for the yoke ;
(2) Its milk yield ; and
(3) The carcase when killed.

Certain points were necessarily of importance in the ox as a draught animal. Weight, size of bone, and thickness of hide were the principal features ; large bone, indicative of strength, and hide which would withstand the chafing of yoke or harness, were manifestly valuable attributes in those days. It must be added that size was of importance for a totally different reason—namely, because the large cattle could better endure the fatigues of travel than smaller beasts.

The following list of modern breeds which were recognised a hundred years ago is of interest. The old authority accepted is Richard Parkinson ; and it may be mentioned that Parkinson's contemporaries recognised and described a larger number of varieties than he did :—

Longhorned, Craven or Lancashire ; Dutch ;* Hereford ; Devonshire ; Sussex ; Galloway or Polled ; † Kyloes ; † Alderney and Welsh.

The Dutch are now known as Shorthorns ; the Devonshire is divided into two breeds—the Devon and South Devon—and the Alderneys are now known as Jerseys. I am not sure that it is quite correct to regard " Kyloes " and " Highland " cattle as the same breed ; the former term was somewhat loosely employed, and is said to be derived

* Described by George Culley as the " Short-horned or Dutch."

† *See* note on p. 68

from the kyles or ferries in the Western Highlands, over which the beasts were swum or carried on their way south to the English grazing-grounds.

The following old breeds are no longer recognised :—

Yorkshire or Teeswater ; Yorkshire Polled ; Suffolk Duns ; Irish ; Shetland ; Fife ;* Argyle ;* and Norland or North Country.*

The following were not recognised, or were not known by their modern names, a hundred years ago :—

Lincolnshire Red Shorthorns, Red Polled, Aberdeen-Angus, Ayrshire, Kerries, and Dexters.

LONGHORNED CATTLE

" This breed," says Marshall,† "appears to have occupied for a length of time the central parts of the island." It was the beast found in the shires—Warwick, Stafford, Derby, Leicester, Lancaster, and part of York—whence it had gone to Westmoreland.

---

* These three, together with the Galloway and Kyloes mentioned on p. 67, were known as Scotch Droving Cattle

† *Rural Economy of the Midland Counties* (1796)

Various districts had each their own breed, distinguishable in some way from those of other districts, but all having the same general character.

In 1791 little progress had been made towards improvement, except in Leicestershire, where Mr. Bakewell had developed the Dishley herd, and on Mr. Fowler's farm, Rollright, in Oxfordshire, where the owner had brought his herd to a state of great perfection. It is to be noticed that both Bakewell and Fowler owed something of their success to the labours of a predecessor, Mr. Webster, of Canley, near Coventry, who, about 1730-50, was the leading breeder in the Midlands. Bakewell's famous bull Twopenny was out of a Canley cow, and the Rollright cows were of the Canley blood.*

With the exception of the herds owned by Messrs. Bakewell, Fowler, Princep, and, no doubt, some others less renowned, the average standard of the breed was not a high one. Its merit was the predisposition to fatten readily, which gave it high rank as "graziers' stock"; as dairy cattle the cows were less esteemed.

* *Rural Economy of the Midland Counties* (1796)

The Longhorns had their resolute admirers, who would allow nothing against them, and claimed that they were as profitable to the dairyman as to the grazier; but the weight of opinion was not in their favour.

The Craven district of Yorkshire, the southern border of Westmoreland, and the north-western corner of Lancashire had long been famous for the superiority of the Longhorns bred there—whence one of the names of the breed—but it was reserved for Bakewell to win fame for the Longhorn as an improved breed, and establish its connection with the Midlands as such.

SHORTHORN CATTLE

The Shorthorn is of mixed origin; it owes something to the old Yorkshire or Teeswater breed, and to the Dutch importations of Mr. Michael Dobinson, to whose influence Culley attached so much importance.

Any attempt to review the gradual rise of the Shorthorn would occupy too much space; * and it must suffice to say that when our period had been reached it was firmly

* *History of Shorthorn Cattle* By J. Sinclair (1908)

SHORTHORN BULL

Presented to King William IV by Sir Charles Morgan, Bart., April, 1836

Painted by J. H. Carter

established, owing largely to the labours of Mr. Charles Colling. He made many experiments in cross-breeding before he arrived at the "Improved Shorthorn," with which the name is identified.

It may be noticed that Colling's work was made known very widely through the famous Durham Ox, which had been sold in 1801 to Mr. John Day. This beast, whose live weight was 216 stone, or 1 ton 7 cwt., was carried about the country in a van for nearly six years, and shown in various parts of the country, until an accident compelled his owner to destroy him. He was thus made an advertisement of the breed.

Mr. Colling's sale of Improved Short-horned Cattle, on the 11th October, 1810, formed an epoch in the history of British cattle-breeding. The details may be briefly summarised :—

Seventeen cows were sold for £2,802 9s. ; eleven bulls, £2,361 9s. ; seven bull calves, £687 15s. ; seven heifers, £942 18s. ; five heifer calves under one year, £321 6s. ; the whole herd—namely, forty-seven head— realising £7,115 17s.

All the bull calves and heifers and three of the heifer calves were got by Comet, son of Favourite. Comet brought the highest figure, £1,000; his son, Petrarch, 365 guineas. Lily, by Comet, fetched the highest price among the cows, 410 guineas; Countess (by Cupid), 400 guineas; Lady went for 206 guineas, being at that time fourteen years old.

Breeders began to recognise that it paid better to rear cattle which would fatten at an early age than those which would grow to great size, and this quality of the Improved Shorthorn was the secret of its rapid advance to popularity. The Shorthorn Herd Book was established in 1822.

The largest and heaviest oxen of this breed were killed and the meat salted to victual the East India ships; they produced the thickest beef, which, by retaining its juices, was the best adapted for long sea voyages.

HEREFORD CATTLE

The origin of this breed is lost in obscurity. The first writer to refer to it is John Speed,* in 1627, whose mention of the number and merits of Herefordshire cattle indicate that the breed was well established in his day. The eighteenth century authorities, Culley and

---

* *England, Wales and Scotland Described* (1627)

Marshall, held somewhat diverse views concerning its origin, and since their time various theories have been put forward.

It was left to careful investigators of our own time to collect the available evidence and reconcile statements which seem to be conflicting. Messrs. Macdonald and Sinclair,* having set out and weighed the several accounts of the breed given by previous writers, have applied thereto the knowledge acquired by eminent naturalists, and arrive at the conclusion that the breed was founded on a variety of the aboriginal cattle of England, "of the type from which the Devon and Sussex breed have been derived"—a conclusion which recalls Marshall's view that the Hereford was akin to those breeds, among others.

As regards the characteristic colour, Messrs. Macdonald and Sinclair find reason to believe that it was originally a whole red, the bald face being a more modern development which can be accounted for by consideration of the local circumstances.

The fact that Herefordshire is on the borders of Wales, where there existed a race of white cattle which were larger than the

---

* *History of Hereford Cattle* (Revised Edition, 1909) Edited by James Sinclair

breed under notice, would explain the tendency to white markings by the crossings which must frequently have taken place. And the introduction by Lord Scudamore (who died in 1671) of Flanders cattle, red bodied and white faced, would further tend to perpetuate the characteristic white face.

The superior size of the Herefordshire over the related breeds, the Devon and Sussex, is also attributable to these crossings of Welsh white cattle at an earlier period, and of Flanders cattle at a later date. The great improvement in the breed is traced by Mr. Thomas Knight, of Downton Castle, to the excellence of those Flanders cattle which were imported by Lord Scudamore.

Mr. Thomas Knight, who died in 1838, was a famous breeder of Herefords ; he took a keen and intelligent interest in the history of the breed, and much importance is attached to his opinion on the subject.

The Hereford was considered one of the best beasts for heavy draught, by reason of its size and weight. It was also very hardy. Mr. Ducket, who had care of the Duke of Bedford's very various cattle, told Arthur Young,* when he visited Woburn in 1797, that the Herefords required more work than any other breed to reduce them in flesh. They were bred in Herefordshire, principally as draught cattle.

DEVON CATTLE

This breed was held in great repute as a draught beast, particularly for the plough on the light soils. It was smaller and more nimble than the Hereford or Sussex, and was the fastest walker of any.

As milkers Devons were much in request. Mr. Conyers,* of Copt Hall, Essex, a gentleman who was much addicted to experiment with various breeds of cattle and sheep (his preference for Welsh sheep has been noticed on page 56), liked Devons better than any other he had tried. "They hold their milk longer, are liable to fewer disorders in their bags, are of small size and do not eat more than half what cows of a larger size consume." The Devon also fattened well and made good beef.

* This gentleman's son, Mr. H. J. Conyers, was Master of the Essex Foxhounds 1805-8, jointly with Mr. Archer Houblon 1813-18, and alone 1818-1853.

The Sussex cattle were famed as a draught breed, but the methods of the Sussex farmer seem to have been peculiar to that county. Holding that it would retard the growth of the cattle to make them exert their full strength in drawing, it was the custom to use from eight to fourteen in a single plough.* Eight oxen comprised a team, and on stiff land this was reinforced by the addition of two or three additional yoke.

In size the Sussex came between the Hereford and the Devon, to both of which it bore considerable resemblance. It had high reputation as a beef breed, but we read little of it in connection with the dairy. Culley observes that it gave less milk than the Suffolk, but of richer quality. It was a hardy breed, and throve on indifferent pasture.

Arthur Young, who paid a visit to Sussex in 1790, was struck by the bad results which had been brought about by crossing. It was the universal opinion, he says, that crossing was necessary for the mere sake of crossing, and he rode nearly 300 miles before he found a bull and a few cows which pleased him even

* *Annals of Agriculture* (Vol. 22)

tolerably. " It is shocking to see the quantity of ugly, big-boned, ill-made homebreds that are everywhere met with."

It is needless to say that the breed has undergone a great change for the better since Young wrote thus. The modern Sussex is the recognised beef type, which matures early and fattens readily.

GALLOWAY OR POLLED CATTLE

" The most essential difference," says an old authority, "between this and every other breed of cattle is in having no horns at all." It was small, generally weighing from 40 to 60 stone, but stood in high repute as a grazier's beast.

A few Galloways were kept in some parts of England, but south of the Tweed it was only seen in numbers at the Norfolk and Suffolk fairs. St. Faiths, near Norwich, was a famous rendezvous for the Scotch Droving Cattle, where they were bought by the graziers and fattened. Few cattle, or none, brought so high a price in Smithfield Market, which was the destination of most of them. They were known in England almost entirely as graziers' beasts, but were moderately good milkers also.

SCOTCH DROVING CATTLE

As already said, the term "Kyloes" was somewhat loosely employed, as it was applied to others than the true Highland breed. Culley refers to "that pure unmixed, valuable breed of Kyloes which we meet with in the more Northern and Western Highlands and all the Isles, but particularly in the Isle of Skye and that tract of country called Kintail." The same authority appears to have had these in mind when he described the Kyloe as being from 20 to 35 stone in weight, generally black in colour and covered with a long close coat of hair.

Great numbers of Kyloes were driven southward every autumn, most finding their way to Norfolk, Suffolk, Essex, and other southern counties to be fattened.

The Northland or Norland cattle would have included those now known as "Aberdeen Angus." A breed of polled cattle has existed for a very long time in the Angus District of Forfarshire, and also in the Buchan district of Aberdeenshire. There is evidence to show that, a hundred years ago, a considerable proportion of the cattle in these districts was hornless; and during the latter part of the eighteenth century some care and skill was devoted to the improvement of the breed.*

In the earlier years of the last century, the Messrs. Williamson, large cattle dealers in Scotland, used to sell about 8,000 head per year to be driven south for disposal; and of these two-thirds were beasts raised in Aberdeenshire.

The then Duke of Gordon, about 1800-1830, brought polled bulls and cows from Galloway into the Buchan district, and these did something to improve the local breed.

The great improvement, however, is attributed to the introduction of the turnip husbandry, sown grasses and general advance in agriculture.† The breed, which is sometimes black or brindled, was held well adapted for grazing purposes ; its merits were recognised by the Highland Society in 1829, in which year prizes were offered for polled cattle at the Show held in Perth.

The first volume of the Aberdeen Angus Herd Book was published in 1862.

---

* *Polled Aberdeen or Angus Breed of Cattle.* By J. Macdonald and J. Sinclair.

† *Agricultural Survey of Aberdeenshire.* By Dr. Skene Keith (1813)

The Rev. William Gilpin,* in his *Observations on Several Parts of the Counties of Cambridgeshire, Norfolk, Suffolk and Essex*, in 1769, says of the meadows on the banks of the Waveney :—

" Here, besides the cattle of the country, numerous herds of starved cattle from the Highlands of Scotland find their way. Of such pasturage they had no idea. Here they lick up the grass by mouthfuls ; the only contention is which of them can eat the most and grow fat the soonest. When they have gotten smooth coats and swagging sides they continue their journey to the capital and present themselves in Smithfield, where they find many admirers."

Mr. George Smith, an old resident of Bow, speaks of " droves of cattle half a mile long," from Norfolk or Suffolk, passing through that part of London on their way to Smithfield.

" They usually passed through Bow on Sunday morning, and went on to the King Harry ' Layers,' a wide open space where they lay down to rest. On Monday

---

* This gentleman was a brother of the famous animal painter, Saurey Gilpin, R.A., of whose life and works an account has been given by me in Vol. 1 of *Animal Painters of England* (Vinton & Co., 1899)

they were driven in to Smithfield market and sold."

Culley observes that the

" demand for Kyloes in England is of vast importance to those nobility and gentry who have estates in the North of Scotland, as most of their rents are paid in live cattle."

JERSEY AND GUERNSEY CATTLE

The name "Alderney" was applied to all Channel Island cattle, whether they came from Jersey, Guernsey or Alderney. In 1785 the Rev. Mr. Valpy visited Jersey, and stated that no less than 120 were exported to England in June of that year.

They were only kept by nobility and gentry for the sake of their peculiarly rich milk. Lord Braybrooke, who lived in the early part of the last century, had, at Audley End, Saffron Walden, a herd of Jerseys, and this was in existence until within recent years.

In 1785 they were, however, to some extent appreciated, and many were imported from the islands.

Mr. John Thornton * says that the annual export from the island at the beginning of the

---

* History of the Breed—*The English Jersey Herd Book* (Vol. 1, 1880)

last century was 400 head. The probability
is that the cattle were shipped only during the
summer months ; so the 120 head mentioned
by Mr. Valpy as exported during June, 1785,
would not represent the average monthly
shipments.

It may be said that no cattle have made
such headway as the Jerseys and Guernseys ;
the exports from the island have increased
until now the number sent to this country,
America and elsewhere reaches 2,000 head
yearly. About 1,800 of these come to
England.

They now rank among the very best dairy
cattle by reason of the richness of their milk.
Many dairy farmers keep only Jerseys, and
their popularity is further shown by the
numbers exhibited at the Agricultural Shows
throughout England. The Jersey class is
usually larger than that of most other breeds.
At the "Royal" at Gloucester in 1909 there
were no fewer than 195 entries of Jerseys
and Guernseys, a total only exceeded by the
Shorthorns, of which there were 422 entries.
The breed that most nearly approached the
Jerseys and Guernseys was the Hereford, of
which there were 91 entries.

The number of exhibits in any class
depends to some extent upon the place where

the "Royal" is held. Thus we should expect to find more Jerseys and Guernseys at Gloucester, the headquarters of a large dairy-farming country, than we should when the Show is held in the heart of the grazing country.

WELSH CATTLE

There were various breeds of Welsh cattle. Parkinson thought they might be regarded as two distinct kinds; the larger brown, best suited for the yoke, and the smaller black breed, known at a later date as the " Pem-brokeshire." These latter were good milkers and had great aptitude to fatten. The Pembrokeshire was regarded as a good " poor man's cow," by reason of its ability to thrive on poor pasture and endure a trying climate.

YORKSHIRE AND YORKSHIRE POLLS

The Yorkshire or Teeswater were famed as a milch breed. One authority describes the cows as by far the best milkers in the United Kingdom. If the horns were yellowish, with black spots, this was considered a good point, as "indicating a great aptitude to fatten."

The Yorkshire Polls differed only from the Yorkshire in having no horns. They were particularly valued by the London dairymen, and the great majority of the 12,000 cows kept in and about the metropolis for milking purposes, at this period, were Yorkshire Polls.

The hide of both these Yorkshire breeds was thin, more especially that of the latter— a fact which rendered them unsuitable for draught.

The Yorkshire beef, like the Shorthorns, was in much request for salting purposes.

SUFFOLK DUNS

The Suffolk Dun, a polled breed of small size, was well thought of. Arthur Young * writes in terms of the highest praise of the dairy cattle he saw in Suffolk :—

> "The quantity of milk they yield exceeds that of any other breed I have ever met with in the kingdom. There is hardly a dairy of any consideration in the country that does not contain cows which give, at the beginning of June, eight gallons of milk in the day ; and six gallons are common among many for a large part of the season."

---

* *Annals of Agriculture* (Vol. 5)

Arthur Young attributed, to some extent, their large milk-yield to the system of feeding. He did not find a single dairy farm in the northern parts of Suffolk without crops of cabbages and turnips which were raised for the cows.

About the middle of the last century the demand for cattle of large carcase became general, and this demand proved the ruin of the Suffolk breed. In their endeavour to enlarge the carcase, the breeders gradually lost the excellent dairy qualities which distinguished these cattle. Had this unfortunate mistake not been made, there can be no doubt but the Suffolk would have become *the* milch cow among English breeds.

AYRSHIRES

The Ayrshire cattle of this time were very indifferent. They are described* as small, ill-fed, ill-shaped, and very poor milkers ; they were usually black with large stripes of white, the horns high and crooked. The work of improving the Ayrshires was taken in hand, and in the 'thirties great advance had been made.

* *General View of the Agriculture of the County of Ayr.* By William Aiton, 1811.

At the present time, Ayrshires rank high as milk producers, and in this respect nearly approach the Channel Island cattle.

KERRY AND DEXTER CATTLE

Parkinson describes two kinds of Irish cattle—the large and long-horned, the best of which weighed as much as 1,400 lbs, and the "Connaught" beasts, which scaled up to 980 lbs.

The small Dexters now imported from Ireland have been judiciously crossed for many years past. They have now a separate Herd Book. The Kerry is higher on the leg than the Dexter; it is regarded as a larger producer of milk.

Owing to the demand for small joints in preference to large, both these breeds meet with more ready sale to the butcher than any larger beast.

IRISH CATTLE TRADE WITH ENGLAND

The huge trade in live-stock between Ireland and England is of modern growth. A hundred and forty years ago this trade had scarcely begun. "Cows, bulls and horses" were summed up together in the official returns, and from them we learn that, in 1771, the total number of cattle and horses brought to England from Ireland was only 1,298 head. In 1777 the number had risen to 5,640 head. In this connection it must be said that the product of Irish pastures was sent to England as beef, of which about 200,000 barrels were shipped every year.

Marshall states that 36,000 head of cattle were sent to England in 1795, and, if his figures are correct, they show that marked advance in the business had taken place in eighteen years.

The trade in live cattle nowadays is large and increasing. During the five years 1876-1880 England received an average of 681,550 beasts per year, more than half of which were for fattening or breeding purposes. And, during the five years 1901-1905, England received an average of 804,204 cattle per year, more than half of which were for fattening or breeding.

It is only just to add that much of the credit for the improvement in Irish stock-breeding which has taken place during the last fifty years is due to my friend, the late Mr. John Thornton, the celebrated cattle salesman.

DRIVING SCOTCH CATTLE TO ENGLAND

In the days before the railway this was an important feature of the cattle industry. Great herds of Scotch cattle were brought south to be fattened on the rich pastures of Norfolk, Lincolnshire and other eastern counties.

The only figures I have been able to discover relating to these annual importations of cattle from Scotland occur in Mr. George Mackenzie's *Essay on Breeding Cattle*,* written in 1780. In the course of his remarks he says that "from Galloway and Ayrshire about 30,000 cattle are sent to England;" but the fact that five breeds (*see* pp. 67 and 68) were known as "droving cattle" sufficiently indicates the magnitude of this trade.

Scotch cattle were very popular with the London butchers, and the animals which had been fattened on English pastures formed a large proportion of the beasts killed annually at Smithfield—152,660 cattle were sold in the year 1808. Animals for the London market were collected and brought up from the country by drovers, who, in some cases, were mounted on ponies.

---

* *Annals of Agriculture* (Vol. 40)

Herds moving from one place to another were not always conducted along the main roads, but by recognised tracks over the wastes, as far as these permitted. These tracks may still be traced in some parts of England, and retain names indicating their old purpose. The walled enclosures in which the herds were penned for the night also remain in various places.

The drovers engaged in this business deserve a few words. They were a hardy, independent class of men, who kept themselves very much to themselves. The responsibility attaching to their work of convoying large herds of cattle safely from one end of the kingdom to the other gave them a certain standing; and reliable drovers, who could deliver the herds without loss, in good condition and without undue delay, made a good living.

They were paid so much per head for every beast delivered, and capable men sometimes made money at the business. Making allowance for the difference in value of money, the cost of sending cattle by road 100 years ago was practically twice that of sending them by rail at the present time. "Amid all the dearness of English inns," says a writer,* in 1796, "oxen are driven

---

* *Annals of Agriculture* (Vol. 29)

from Dumfries to London, 450 miles, for 18*s.* to 24*s.*"*

The greater number of cattle fatted for the markets of London and the South of England came from Scotland and the northern counties of England, and many drovers were engaged in the business. They were, for the most part, Scotchmen, who practically spent their lives on the road, carrying with them little besides a bag of oatmeal.

It is necessary to distinguish between the drover and the jobber. The former conducted cattle belonging to his patrons, charging so much per head for the journey. The jobber, or dealer, was very frequently a man who had made money as a drover, and bought cattle from the farmers outright, to sell for his own profit at distant fairs and markets.

It may be mentioned that there are now residing in Norwich and the neighbourhood many families of Scottish origin, the descendants of Scottish drovers and jobbers who settled there when they gave up active work on the road.

---

* The railway rate for a truck containing from eight to six beasts, according to size, by goods train from Dumfries to London is now £6 17*s.* 9*d.*, which works out at from 17*s.* 6*d.* to 23*s.* per head.

Those drovers or jobbers who bought and sold on their own account had matters very much their own way in dealing with the farmers and graziers in some districts.

In 1793 Mr. J. H. Campbell, of Kings Down, Bristol, stated* that when he had endeavoured to induce his neighbours in Pembrokeshire to improve their cattle—

> "the answer of one and all was, ' We must breed what the drovers will give most money for ; and they all tell us they will not buy any but black.' Some have told me that they have had a brown ox of my sort which, in their own opinion, was at least as good a beast as any black one they had, and yet they were forced to take it as a favour that the drover would buy him at an inferior price to the others ; and assured them that had he been black they could have afforded to give them 20 or 25 per cent. more on him."

The wandering life no doubt had its own attraction, and drovers who could afford to retire from the road often continued in the saddle until an advanced age. Women were sometimes employed as drovers in the Midland and home counties ; they followed the cattle on foot. It may be observed that,

---

* *Annals of Agriculture* (Vol. 21)

under an old statute (3 Chas. I), cattle might not be driven on Sunday.

Some of the London distillers at this period used to buy large numbers of oxen at the fairs—more especially at Kingston-on-Thames—and fatten them on the "grains" for the butcher. The Hereford and the largest of the Welsh cattle were preferred for this purpose.

THE CARRIER'S CART, DRAWN BY EIGHT HORSES

HORSES

It is hardly necessary to insist upon the importance of the place held by horses of all kinds before the railway days. The roads of the kingdom a hundred years ago, although improving, were still in a very bad state, more especially the district and cross roads. Arthur Young's description of these latter, in his *Tour in the North of England* (1770),*

---

* " I know not, in the whole range of language, terms sufficiently expressive to describe this infernal road. To look over a map, and perceive that it is a principal one, not only to some towns, but even whole counties, one would naturally conclude it to be at least decent; but let me most seriously caution all travellers who may accidentally purpose to travel this terrible country, to avoid it as they would the devil, for a thousand to one but they break their necks or their limbs by overthrows or breakings down. They will here meet with ruts, which I actually measured, four feet deep, and floating with mud, only from a wet summer; what, therefore, must it be after the winter? The only mending it receives, in places, is the tumbling in loose stones, which serve no other purpose but jolting the carriage in a most intolerable manner. These are not merely opinions, but facts, for I actually passed three carts broken down in these eighteen miles of execrable memory."

was still applicable to very many country highways.

The great main roads were fairly good, and the number of coaches plying over long and short stages was increasing. The brief "golden age" of the road had not yet dawned, but the coaching industry required great numbers of horses.

Apart from coaching, every country gentleman drove or rode. The farmer and commercial traveller travelled on horseback or drove a gig. Goods, in out-of-the-way parts of England, were still carried on strings of packhorses. The importance of the packhorse as a means of transport in old days is shown by the old "packhorse bridges" still remaining over the streams in various parts of England. These are wide enough to allow a laden horse to pass, but too narrow for carts. The canal boats which carried heavy merchandise were towed by horses; and a great deal of the work of the farm was done by horses, sometimes by mixed teams of horses and oxen.

Large numbers of horses also were required by our troops in Portugal and Spain during the Peninsular War, 1808-14. Many were obtained in those countries, but the majority had to be sent out from England,

OLD PACKHORSE BRIDGE AT SUTTON, BEDS.

and the demand for these lent a stimulus to breeding, more especially in the northern counties, which resulted in large production.

In works written after the close of the Peninsular War, references are made to the effect which cessation of hostilities had had upon the horse-breeding industry.

The Spanish horses, which in earlier ages had been so greatly in request among English horse-breeders,* were less valued.

Arabs, also, were much less in request for breeding race-horses than they had been fifty years earlier. How little the Eastern stallion was used at this time is shown by the list of " Stallions to Cover in England in 1809," given in the *Sporting Magazine* of that year (Vol. 33). Of 85 sires only three are Arabs.

The highest service fees asked for English Thoroughbred sires were 50 guineas (Gohanna) and 25 guineas (Beningborough), whereas the Elgin Arabian and Mahomet were offered at 3 guineas each. It may be remarked that all the three Arabs in the list stood in Yorkshire.

---

* The Duke of Newcastle, in his great work written in 1658, says: " I have seen Spanish horses which were proper to be painted, or fit for a king to mount on a public occasion."

The decline in the use of Spanish and, later, of Arab blood was the result of the vast improvement which had been brought about in our English Throughbreds or " blood horses," as they were then called; for the modern term "Thoroughbred" had not at this period come into use.

THE SHIRE HORSE

This is the modern name of the famous breed which was formerly known as the Great, Large Black, or Heavy Black Horse. It was, above all, *the* cart-horse, and was principally bred in the Midlands—Derby, Leicester, Warwick, Stafford and Lincoln shires—those reared in the last-named county being the largest.

The Black was the best recognised breed of draught horse England possessed. The Ashby Black Stallion Show at Easter, where sires were offered on hire for the season, was an institution. Yearling Blacks were sold at certain markets or fairs devoted specially to them—Ashby, Loughborough, Burton-on-Trent, Rugby, and Ashbourne.

The graziers who bought the yearlings kept them till two or two off, when they sold them to farmers, who worked them lightly in

CHISWELL STREET BREWERY

(From a Painting by G. Garrard, A.R.A.)

the plough and then sold them, ready for work in the London drays.

The distinctive colour of the breed, now known as the " Shire," is gradually disappearing, and a black horse is now the exception in pedigree stock, though the old colour sometimes occurs to remind us of the original strain.*

The Black had had a chequered history. In the days of armour it was the war horse;† when heavy armour was discarded it still furnished remounts to Dragoons, and remained, up to the earlier years of the last century, in some request (though lighter horses were more in demand) for Army purposes.

The Black was also in general use for coach and carriage work when vehicles were weighty and roads bad ; but improvements in carriages and roads led to its disuse.

Various statements have been made concerning improvements in the Black. Lord Chesterfield, when Ambassador (about 1755-60) at the Hague, brought home

---

* *Horses—Breeding to Colour.* By Sir Walter Gilbey, Bart. (Vinton & Co., 1907)

† *The Great Horse or War Horse.* By Sir Walter Gilbey, Bart. (Vinton & Co., 1899)

7

half-a-dozen Zealand mares, which were stabled at Bretby, in Derbyshire.

One of the Earls of Huntingdon brought "a set of coach-horses of the black breed" from the Low Countries. At first he found it difficult to persuade his tenants by Trent-side to send their mares to them ; but when a few foals had been got by these stallions, the breeders at once saw that the youngsters were superior to the foals got by local stock and eagerly sent their mares to the Earl's horses.

Bakewell appears to have believed in these traditions, for he, with Mr. George Salisbury, visited Germany and Holland, and brought home half-a-dozen " Dutch or Flanders Mares." These proved of use in improving the Leicestershire Blacks ; so much so that they became known as " Bakewell's Blacks."

George Culley took some horses of the Bakewell breed to Northumberland, when he went thither to establish himself as a farmer, and these were the means of introducing much-needed improvement into the Northumbrian cart-horses, which appear to have been of nondescript character.

It was the custom of the Midland breeders to use only the mares for farm-work. All were used for breeding, and the geldings

were sold for farm-work in the south and
west, the finest going to London as dray-
horses ; some, according to Culley (1807),
were still sold as Cavalry remounts. Youatt *
says : " A smaller variety, with more blood,
constitutes a considerable part of our
Cavalry."

About the end of the eighteenth century
some Midland farmers began to replace their
Blacks by oxen. When Marshall visited
these parts of England in 1796 the "spirit
for working oxen appeared to be gaining
ground apace among superior managers."

Culley refers to the extraordinary pride
taken by the south country farmers in their
teams of Blacks. He had seen six stallions in
line, each adorned with fringe and tassels,
"enough to half-load a common Yorkshire
cart-horse." The leader of this team wore
six bells, the next five, and so on to the
shaft-horse, which only wore one. Equal
pride in their Black horses was taken by
the London brewers and their men.

THE SUFFOLK PUNCH

This breed, otherwise known as the
" Sorrel," by reason of its distinctive colour,

---

* *The Horse.* By William Youatt (1831)

had for a long period been celebrated for its working qualities. It was peculiar to Suffolk and Norfolk, and was esteemed for strength, activity and endurance.

Arthur Young, who travelled in Suffolk in 1764, 1776 and 1779, thought that the true breed was disappearing when he last visited the county.

The old Suffolk Punch was "yellowish or sorrel" (dun) in colour, with a white blaze ; was punchy in shape and seldom over 15.2 in height ; as a farm horse it had no equal.

Young refers to a Suffolk Punch belonging to Mr. Weeden, which drew 12½ quarters of wheat in a waggon up a hill for more than 12 rods.

There were some good examples of the breed remaining at rather a later period. Daniel * states that, at the sale of Sir Robert Harland's horses in October, 1812, the following prices were realised, showing " the estimation in which Suffolk Punches are held " :—13 horses averaged £32 8s. ; 16 horses averaged £61 4s. ; 4 horses averaged £81 ; 5 horses averaged £140 ; 3 three-year-old colts averaged £53 ; 2 two-year-old colts averaged £51 ; 6 yearlings,

* *Rural Sports* (Supplementary Vol., 1813)

£44 each; and 6 suckers £37 18s. 6d. each.
The value of money in those days must be
borne in mind with reference to these figures.
The prices were equal to about twice the
amount in our own day.

It was the importation of Yorkshire half-
bred sires that did much to change the
character of the Suffolk Punch. The
infusion of this blood wrought increase of
height and size. It also brought about a
change of colour, but the mixed breed
retained many of the good qualities of the
old stock, which is said to have been derived
from Norman stallions put to Suffolk cart-
mares.

Culley has left it on record that the old
Suffolk Punch could plough more land in a
day than any other horse. Other authorities
attribute his speed in the plough to the
lightness of the soil; but, whatever the
truth, there can be no doubt of his merits.
Arthur Young coupled the breed with the
Black, as the only two varieties of cart-
horse in England deserving of mention.

It remains to add that, during the last
fifty years, the Suffolk horse has been
classed as one of the best breeds of heavy
horses in England.

THE CLYDESDALE

The Duke of Hamilton is credited with having imported Flanders stallions about 1600 or a few years later; the breed is said to have been produced by crossing these stallions with common Scotch cart-mares.

The Clydesdale, a hundred years ago, was esteemed a good and useful farmer's horse. Generally grey or brown, it stood from 15 hands to 16.

The Clydesdale was popular in the northern counties of England, whither it had been brought from Scotland; but does not seem to have found its way further south, if we may base an opinion on the absence of reference to it by writers of the time.

During the last fifty years great attention has been paid by breeders to the improvement of the Clydesdale. A Stud Book was established in 1883, and since that date the breed has been kept pure, and it now ranks as one of the best heavy breeds in the Kingdom. Large intakes of blood from Derbyshire had been made at earlier periods.

THE CLEVELAND BAY

The Cleveland Bay enjoyed a reputation for activity, strength and hardiness. Three of these horses, it was said, would draw one-and-a-half tons of coals sixty miles in twenty-four hours, without more rest than two or three baits on the road, and would frequently do this four times a week.

Mr. Lumley Hodgson, of Highthorne, in Yorkshire, writing in 1889, says: "The old-fashioned and, unhappily, virtually extinct Cleveland could ride, hunt, plough, and, to a short-legged Thoroughbred horse, breed the best of Hunters."

A pure-bred Cleveland was usually, if not invariably, a bay with black legs. The process of "swamping" the breed with other blood had been going on for some time before our period.

Marshall, writing in 1783, says that :—

"The Vale, the Wolds, the Holderness (district) probably employ a hundred Thoroughbred stallions ; one hundred mares are considered the full complement for one horse ; some of them, perhaps, do not get fifty. . . . There must have been 10,000 brood-mares in use."

This cross-breeding was done in order to produce coach-horses, also Hunters of greater size, heavy-weight Hunters being at this period in great request.

In 1882, Mr. Thomas Parrington, writing
to Lord Cathcart, said :—

"It is much to be regretted that the
foreigners have been buying them up for
years, until it is now difficult to find such
mares in the hands of farmers."

Of recent years, since Mr. Parrington wrote,
much has been done to restore the breed.
Classes have been allotted to it at Agricultural Shows, and the encouragement given
has produced the most satisfactory results.

The late Mr. Blew * stated that, before the
inauguration of the Cleveland Bay Horse
Society's Stud Book, the foreign demand
did much to keep the breed alive.

THE YORKSHIRE COACH HORSE

In 1886 was established the Yorkshire
Coach Horse Society. Classes are allotted
to Yorkshire Coach Horses at many of the
Shows, but it may be assumed that the breed
is very closely allied to the Cleveland Bay.

THE "BLOOD HORSE"

Of the Thoroughbred or race-horse little
need be said here ; it demands mention by

* *Journal of the Royal Agricultural Society of England*
(Vol. 25, 1889)

reason of the frequency with which it was
used to improve other lighter breeds for the
saddle and also for harness. "Blood"
horses, as they were very generally called,
were much used to get Hunters, coach and
carriage horses.

The Thoroughbred was smaller and
altogether a more suitable horse for
improving other breeds than his modern
descendant.

I have written much on this particular
point, and need not now repeat it.*

THE HUNTER

The Hunter, very usually the produce of
a "blood" sire and roadster, was at this
time a faster horse than the Hunter of
fifty years earlier. This was the result of
improved agricultural methods ; the drainage
of lands was better and more general, hence
scent was better and hounds ran faster,
obliging the hunting man to ride a speedier
horse than had served him in earlier days
when hounds had to pick out the line.

The fields that followed hounds were
much smaller 100 years ago than they are

* *Thoroughbred and other Ponies.*   By Sir Walter
Gilbey, Bart.   (Vinton & Co., 1903)

in our day, and men often rode entire horses. These were used for stud purposes, and thus Hunters were bred from genuine Hunter stock. The result was a recognised race of Hunters celebrated for courage, honesty and stoutness. This " race " was nearly extinct in 1836, if we may accept the evidence of a writer in the *Sporting Magazine* for that year.

Yorkshire and Lincolnshire were great Hunter-breeding counties. Howden, in the former county, was famous for the fair to which " unmade " Hunters were brought for sale by the breeders. Horncastle, in Lincolnshire, was the scene of the greatest fair for " made " Hunters in England.

Breeding Hunters was an important part of the farmer's business in these two counties. Lincolnshire — the Brocklesby country, at least — was said to be full of the stock got by Quicksilver, a stallion owned by the then Earl of Yarborough.

It used to be said that the hack of the Lincolnshire Wolds farmer was a pretty good hunter for other countries. Shropshire was also a famous county for Hunter-breeding at this time.

The old system of Hunter-breeding — namely, breeding from Hunter stock — was attempted by the Hunters' Improvement Society when that body was established in 1885. Its work was pursued and has been carried on with success in spite of much hostile criticism from the many who would still have us believe that only the Thorough-bred sire can be used with certainty in breeding Hunters.

THE ROADSTER

Apart from the Norfolk Hackneys, whose wonderful trotting powers led the east country breeders to keep them apart from the common stock, the Roadster can hardly be considered a distinct breed.

The average road-horse, an indispens-able animal in former times, was usually one with less blood than the Hunter ; if he could carry a fairly heavy weight, trot six or seven miles in the hour, and keep it up for a day of five hours, he was considered to fulfil reasonable requirements, thirty miles a day being as much as the ordinary traveller on a long journey wished to go.

The traveller carried his luggage in a pair of bags, and the horse's load might be as much as eighteen stone.

The farmer's saddle-horse was very commonly an animal of great strength. Those were the days when the pillion was in general use, and the horse was often required to carry a double load—the farmer and his wife.

Fourteen hands to 14 hands 3 inches was considered the best height for the road horse. What was wanted was a compact, sound, willing horse that could walk as well as trot.

The improvement in roads and spread of coaches did something to undermine the important position held by the Roadster, and railways finished what the coaches had begun.

Mr. Lumley Hodgson, the gentleman referred to on a previous page, says that he thought nothing of riding 200 miles, and in his college days always made the journey between Yorkshire and Cambridge on horseback.

The horses employed for mail and stage coach and posting were of very various character. Those which were ridden by the postillions in post-chaises were the best.

Public vehicles, however, were horsed by contractors, and all kinds of horses found their way to the contractor's stables—good, bad, and indifferent.

There were animals, more especially of the
Norfolk Hackney breed, which could trot
their fifteen to eighteen miles within the
hour ; but these were the racers of the road,
and figured more often in sporting matches
than in daily work.

THE WELSH PONY

The writers of a hundred years ago say
little of the Welsh pony, save to praise highly
its hardiness and soundness of limb.   Culley
says :—

> " Few or none can equal them for the
> road, none stand our turnpikes like them,
> and I well remember one that I rode for
> many years, which to the last would have
> gone upon a pavement by choice, in pre-
> ference to a softer road."

Parkinson calls it " the most complete pony
in the kingdom."   Its small size was against
it for heavy agricultural work, and the fact
sufficiently explains the little attention this
breed received at the hands of writers whose
principal object was to make known the
merits of animals most suitable for economical
working of the farm.

Its merits are better understood in our
own day.   Reared, as it is, on the bleak hills

of Wales, its wonderful constitution makes it valuable for many purposes, more especially for crossing with other breeds.*

THE WELSH COB

Until about sixty years ago, attempts to produce, on a basis of Welsh pony blood, a larger animal were few and unimportant; but, since the introduction of small Norfolk Hackney stallions, the breeding of Welsh cobs has been systematically followed, and we see the results at the present day.

When at Llandrindod Wells, I have always been impressed by the make, shape and paces of the Welsh cobs which are to be seen in the town daily, ridden thither from the farms in the surrounding hills by the women who thus bring to market their eggs, butter and other produce.

Sturdy, docile, quick-stepping and sure-footed, these cobs possess all the useful qualities of the small mountain ponies, and, with them, the size—about 14 hands—and power which render them such valuable animals to the agriculturist in country where the roads are often bridle-paths impossible for wheel traffic.

* *Thoroughbred and other Ponies.* By Sir Walter Gilbey, Bart. (Vinton & Co., 1903)

It is a tribute to the worth of the Welsh cob, and its peculiar fitness for the work it is required to do, that breeding these little horses continues to be remunerative.

My late friend, Sir Richard Green Price, was one of those who did much to bring about the improvement in the breed of hill ponies and cobs, and also to make their good qualities more widely known.

THE GALLOWAY

The Galloway, also called the Scotch horse had become rare a century ago ; the value of these small and hardy cobs made their disappearance a matter of regret. Youatt * quotes Dr. Anderson as saying :—

> " There was once a breed of small elegant horses in Scotland similar to those of Iceland and Sweden, known by the name of Galloways, the best of which sometimes reached a height of 14 hands and a half."

Dr. Anderson described one which was given him when a boy. He rode it for five-and-twenty years, and twice during that time made journeys of 150 miles at a stretch without stopping, except to bait the horse for about an hour each time. In its prime, he

---

* *The Horse* (1831)

said, it could have done 60 miles a day for a twelvemonth without any extraordinary exertion.

Some remarkable feats of endurance by Galloways are on record. Perhaps the most memorable is that quoted by Youatt of one owned by Mr. Sinclair, of Kirkby-Lonsdale, which, at Carlisle, travelled a thousand miles in a thousand hours. It is unfortunate that particulars of this performance have not been recorded.

The term "Galloway" is now used to describe a small horse. The Rules of the Pony and Galloway Racing Association define a Galloway as an animal of not over 15 hands.

FAT PIG

The Property of Mr. William White, Kingston, Surrey

(Killed March, 1798)

PIGS

The pig, a century ago, was engaging more attention than it had ever done before.

Swine were raised on the system prevalent in the early and middle ages, modified as the changed conditions of the country required. The destruction of forests and reclamation of wastes forbade the rearing of swine in a half-wild state, but it was still the farmer's practice to turn his swine on to the stubbles after the crops had been carried.

The Chinese pig had been introduced somewhere about 1770-80 (the date cannot be ascertained with certainty), and had been widely used for crossing with our English breeds.

Numbers of fattening experiments were being made by eminent stock-breeders, and it was realised that judicious cross-breeding and feeding were the means whereby improvement in pork and bacon could be attained.

Hogs of enormous size were sometimes produced and attracted much notice, but

8

rather as curiosities than examples to be taken as models for the breeder.

The desirability of encouraging the poorer classes to keep pigs was well recognised. Among the premiums offered by the Board of Agriculture in 1803 was a gold medal for the person who should build, on his estate, the largest number of labourers' cottages with land to support a cow and a hog.

A very large number of different varieties was recognised at this time. Parkinson* describes no fewer than seventeen, including seven varieties of Chinese pigs; and, he adds, "there are many others."

There was little difference between some of these varieties, which were named after the counties with which they were more or less identified; and it is only reasonable to suppose that there was a good deal of crossing and interbreeding.

An anonymous writer in the *Annals of Agriculture* (Vol. 33, 1799) says:—

"It would be endless to particularise all the breeds of swine there are in England. Those only which deserve our attention are: (1) The Berkshire; (2) Shropshire; (3) Northampton; and (4) Chinese."

---

* *Treatise on Live-Stock* (1810)

THE BERKSHIRE

The Berkshire breed is the only one which has retained its name to the present day ; and it is to be noted that this was the most widely distributed breed a hundred years ago. At that time its most distinctive characteristic was almost the total absence of hair.

The Tamworth district was famous for the pigs raised there, but this name was not applied to it ; on the contrary, Parkinson says that the most famous pigs bred near Tamworth were called " Berkshires."

The Tamworth was described* as spotted red and brown, reaching a great size, having small ears, short legs and very broad sides ; these pigs were held not suitable stock for anyone who could not provide them with abundance of food, as without enough they did not thrive, fell into disease and proved less profitable than a smaller breed.

The breed has undergone considerable modifications during a hundred years. If we compare old and modern pictures of representative animals, the change in the shape of the head is very striking ; the whole shape of the Berkshire has been changed by careful selection.

---

* *Annals of Agriculture* (Vol. 33)

THE SHROPSHIRE

The Shropshire breed was either white or coloured, but usually the former; they had slouch ears, hanging on their cheeks, and short legs.

The Shropshire were much in request at Barnet, a great market in those days, no doubt because they were popular with the London distillers, as they did well on "grains."

Large numbers of swine were then kept by the distillers as a profitable means of disposing of the grains.

THE NORTHAMPTON

The Northampton breed much resembled the Shropshire. They were white and short-legged, distinguished by their huge ears, which "sweep along on the ground before their noses, almost blinding them." This made them "a remarkably gentle breed." These pigs grew to an immense size, especially those reared in the Naseby district of Northamptonshire.

THE CHINESE

There were two varieties of Chinese pig— one very large, the other small. These were used for crossing with other breeds; the larger made most excellent bacon.

The authorities are at variance concerning the hardiness of the Chinese pig. The author of an essay in the *Annals of Agriculture** says they were very hardy and would live on less food by far than any of the three English breeds he considered deserving of attention. They were rarely seen lean or in poor condition; and in his experiments he had found Chinese pigs fatten well on food that would only keep other hogs.

Parkinson says that as they were somewhat delicate and difficult to rear, it did not pay to slaughter them.

The Chinese-Berkshire cross was the one most usual; this was natural, as the Berkshire offered the best material for improvement.

The frequency with which the Societies offered prizes for the best pig of Chinese cross shows how generally the merit of this breed was recognised.

It is strange that the Chinese pig should have so completely disappeared. It has not been known in England during the last fifty years, having been completely merged in our native breeds.

---

* Vol. 33, 1799

118

OTHER BREEDS

The Lincoln and Sussex breeds were esteemed.

Lord Winchelsea, at Burley, in Rutland-shire, kept a herd of Suffolk pigs, white short-nosed, thick small-boned, having a good disposition to fatten.

Arthur Young says Lord Winchelsea found "considerable difficulty in rearing the young, either by reason of their pre-disposition to fatten or for lack of crossing. He lost forty pigs out of fifty between Michaelmas, 1797, and Michaelmas, 1798."

The Cheshire breed was one of the largest, though Yorkshire pigs of great size were occasionally produced.

The Yorkshire breed, from which the three "White" varieties recognised at the present day trace their descent, was popular as a distiller's pig at this time.

A considerable number of pigs of different breeds were sent to America a hundred years ago to improve the stock in that country. The Berkshire are said to have been in request.

The Irish pig, once lean and leggy, was improving. At Ballinasloe Fair, in 1802, it was remarked that the improvement in the breed of swine was "truly surprising."

In view of the number of pigs which were kept in England 100 years ago, it is a curious fact that pork, for a long period, was the dearest meat on the market. Pork was $8\frac{1}{2}d.$ per pound when beef was $5\frac{1}{2}d.$ and mutton $7\frac{3}{4}d.$

For many years now pig-breeding in Ireland has been a profitable industry. The best and finest bacon comes to England from Belfast.

BACON FACTORIES

If bacon factories should be established in England, as they have been in Denmark with the best results, pig-breeders should bear in mind that the long-snouted kinds are the most suitable ; they should be kept until they are from 15 to 18 months old.

INTELLIGENCE OF THE PIG

The following curious example of the tractability of pigs is worth reproducing. One day, in October, 1811—

"A man who holds a small farm near St. Alban's, and who has ever been looked upon as a most eccentric being, made his appearance into the latter place in the following manner, viz., mounted on a small car which was drawn by four large hogs.

"He entered the town at a brisk trot, amidst the acclamations of hundreds, who were soon drawn together to witness this uncommon spectacle. After making the tour of the Market Place three or four times, he came into the Wool-Pack Hotel yard, had his swinish cattle regularly un-harnessed and taken into a stable together, where they were regaled with a trough full of beans and swill. They remained about two hours, whilst he dispatched his business as usual at the market, when they were put to and driven home again, multitudes cheering him.

"This man had only had these animals under training six months, and it is truly surprising to what a high state of tracta-bility he has brought them. A gentleman on the spot offered him fifty pounds for the concern as it stood, but it was indignantly refused." *

One of the most remarkable examples of the point to which the intelligence of the pig can be cultivated is furnished by the famous "pig pointer." This was a black sow which two King's keepers in the New Forest, Toomer by name, trained in a fortnight to find game, point and back almost as well as a pointer.

* *Daniel's Rural Sports* (Supplementary Vol., 1813)

The excellent scenting powers of the pig are, as is well known, utilised by French truffle-finders, who train young swine to find the truffles buried, as they are, a few inches below the soil. They were used for this purpose in England also ; Lord Braybrooke kept truffle-hunting pigs some fifty years ago.

POULTRY

TURKEYS

A writer in the *Annals of Agriculture* *
observes that turkeys pay as well as, or better
than, any other birds for the amount of
attention given them.   He says :—

> " Any farm not very small may keep one
> cock and six hens, and they rarely fail of
> bringing many young ones, as they set very
> steadily, scarcely ever leaving their eggs."

Richard Parkinson † says that in Ireland
the poorer people raised " an amazing number
of very fine turkeys," rearing them on milk or
butter-milk, into which shredded nettles were
mixed, and a little oatmeal mixed to a paste.
This food was cheap, and the turkey-raising
business paid.

Fine turkeys were raised on the Lincolnshire marshes and also in Norfolk.   The
bronze or copper-coloured and the white

---

* Vol. 39, 1803.

† Richardson Parkinson was the author of three
works on Agriculture, published in 1807, 1810
and 1811.

varieties were regarded as distinct. It was thought that the former were wilder and more prone to stray than the latter, and this was attributed to their being "more freely bred from the wild turkeys" imported from America.

The cheapest method of fattening was by "cramming" them with barley meal made into paste with milk, butter-milk or pot-liquor.

Parkinson mentions that there was to be seen in Leadenhall Market a turkey weighing 30 lbs., for which the salesman asked 2 guineas.

It is a question if this turkey could have been what is now termed a "stag"—that is to say, a year-old bird.

GEESE

Geese were held the most profitable kind of poultry. They were raised in vast numbers in the Lincolnshire fens. Pennant says that a single person would keep as many as 1,000 old birds, each of which raising seven goslings, the owner at the year's end would find himself master of a flock of 8,000 birds.

On the great tracks of fenland, before they were drained, over a thousand persons made their living out of geese.

Geese were extensively bred also in Norfolk, Suffolk, Cornwall and the Aylesbury district of Buckinghamshire. Some farmers believed that geese were injurious to the pastures; writers on the subject contradict this idea, however, maintaining that geese were not only harmless but beneficial.

In the Midland counties it was believed by some that geese were "healthful things" among cows, and many farmers made a point of keeping a flock, the idea being that the birds purified the water of the pond where the cattle drink.

The importance of goose-rearing appears in the name of the "Nottingham Goose Fair," so-called because held at the time of year when geese are ready for market, and great numbers were brought for sale by the country people. The Nottingham Fair dates from 1283-4; geese have long ceased to be a speciality, however.

The profit of goose-keeping lay in the practice of plucking. In the Lincolnshire fens the feathers were the principal object, and it was usual to pluck the birds five times a year, at intervals of six weeks, beginning at Lady-day.

The value of the goose feathers was estimated at about a shilling a head per year, and threepence more for the quills, at that time in general demand for pens.

The feathers from live geese fetched a better price than those taken from dead birds, and if the process of plucking were done at the right time, when the feathers were "ripe" and came away easily, there was no cruelty in the operation

Geese shed their plumage three times a year, and our fathers regarded it as wanton waste to allow the feathers to drop of themselves.

In many parts of France goose-plucking is still practised.

Geese were fattened for the market on oats and water, or boiled carrots or potatoes, when special treatment was thought desirable.

Fattening geese was a distinct department of the industry; it was practised by farmers who made a speciality of collecting the birds and feeding them up.

The Messrs. Bagshaw, of Norwich, were well-known in this connection, and they carried on the goose-fattening business for many years.

In the early part of the last century, Messrs. Bagshaw used to import great numbers of geese from Ireland and Holland and fatten them for the Michaelmas and Christmas markets. The Dutch geese, so-called, were for the most part brought to Holland from

Russia, and were shipped from Rotterdam to Norwich.

Mr. R. G. Bagshaw, the present head of the firm, informs me that he used to visit Northern Germany in search of geese, which he purchased from people who travelled about the country collecting them. Harwich was the port to which the birds were sent, and the early part of October was the time when the majority arrived.

About thirty or forty years ago, Messrs. Bagshaw fattened every year from ten to fifteen thousand geese for Christmas and about 2,000 for Michaelmas.

The large "goose clubs," supported by working-men in London, were prominent among their regular customers at that time, but the firm no longer supply these clubs. The demand for geese has fallen off enormously of late years.

Vast numbers of geese and turkeys were brought to London from the great breeding areas of the Eastern counties.

Defoe* says that in one season—August to

---

* Daniel Defoe, who died in 1731, though best known as the author of *Robinson Crusoe*, was the author of numerous works, among them *A Tour through the Island*, written in 1722, which contains much information concerning agriculture and live-stock.

October—as many as 300 droves of turkeys, each of which might number 500 to 1,000 birds, would pass over Stratford Bridge on their way to London. The geese fed on the stubbles by the way.

The Rev. W. B. Daniel mentions that in 1793 a single drove, numbering over 9,000 geese, passed through Chelmsford.

I remember, in the year 1840, once seeing hundreds of droves of turkeys and geese on the old coach road at Bishop Stortford slowly travelling towards London. This was before the Great Eastern Railway was constructed.

Each drove numbered about a thousand and was conducted by two men, each of whom carried a long slender pole with a red flag on the top; with this implement he guided and marshalled the birds on their way.

An odd wager made in 1740 in connection with the travelling powers of geese and turkeys is worth recalling. Geese being much the slower walkers, Lord Orford bet the Duke of Queensberry that a drove of these would reach London from Norwich much sooner than a drove of turkeys which started at the same time. The Duke lost the wager. The turkeys, as Lord Orford knew they would, flew up into the trees at dusk to roost, and their drivers found great difficulty in

dislodging them to resume the journey.
The geese, on the other hand, continued their
journey in the dark and arrived at their
destination two days before the turkeys.

FOWLS

Various breeds of fowls were raised.
The Dorking and Poland were kept as farm
stock, and, in the Midlands, game fowls
were held superior to other breeds as egg-
producers and for the table.

Game fowls, it is hardly necessary to
remark, were kept by persons in all ranks of
life for cock-fighting. Mrs. Stirling, in
an interesting essay contributed to the
Nineteenth Century and After (April, 1908),
entitled " Fresh Light on Coke of Norfolk,"
says of life at Holkham : " On days when it
was too wet to shoot, cock-fighting took place
in the portico, and the guests sat at the large
window to watch it." It is only necessary to
glance at the old *Sporting Magazine* to see
how large a place cock-fighting held among
our ancestors at this time.

Game fowls were popularly known as
" Shake-bags." This term has reference
to a usage of the cockpit. The usual
method was to match cock against cock

by weight, the birds being carefully
weighed that each might be pitted
against a foe of equal weight. On
occasion it would be arranged that the
cocks first taken, or shaken, out of the
bags in which they were conveyed to the
pit should fight one another. Hence the
term " Shake-bag."

The writer in the *Annals of Agriculture*
before referred to mentions " the common
white—that is, large with white legs"—and
the Dorking as the two best.

Dorkings were in great demand for the
London market. They were famous, and
the art of fattening them was " a sort of trade
or mystery " concerning which the initiated
preserved secrecy.

North Chappel and Kenford, in Sussex,
and Oaking, in Berkshire, were famed as
fowl-rearing centres.

Little attention was bestowed on the
ordinary fowls of the farmyard; indeed, an
authority of 1781, though he describes them
as " a necessary part of the stock of a farm
which yield considerable service and profit
by their eggs, brood, feathers, dung, &c.,"
recommends them as being cheap to maintain, inasmuch as they can support themselves

9

the greater part of the year and may be kept
"near any highway side."

In the days when wheat paid the farmer
and wool brought a high price, it was not
worth his while to spend time and trouble
over such a small matter as poultry-keeping.

Of late years the demand for poultry and
eggs has greatly increased ; and, in spite of
the heavy importations of both from foreign
countries, farmers and cottagers are devoting
much more attention to the rearing of fowls
and production of eggs than they did formerly.
The increasing importance of the industry
induced me to publish a little work on the
subject.*

DUCKS

Ducks were regarded as profitable stock
by reason of the small amount of care they
required, and the eagerness with which they
consume harmful grubs, &c. "The best,"
says our authority in the *Annals of
Agriculture*, "are the wild breed which is
domesticated on many farms, and the largest
is the French Rouen Duck."

* *Poultry Keeping on Farms and Small Holdings.* By
Sir Walter Gilbey, Bart. (Vinton & Co., 1906)

The practice of rearing ducklings under hens was recommended. The duck was likely to swim three-fourths of a large brood to death, if she were not kept out of the water in a coop ; also, the ducklings were likely to be destroyed by crows if allowed to remain about ponds where there was little cover to conceal them.

Dark colour in ducks was held an advantage, as the ducklings were not so quickly seen by crows, hawks, gleads,* &c.

The Aylesbury district, then as now, was famous as a duck-raising centre. The birds, for the most part of the white variety, were reared for the Christmas market.

Duck-breeders kept the birds in their cottages to promote the production of eggs. Parkinson says :—

"They are commonly admitted into their bedrooms, under the beds, at night, and some rest in the kitchen fire corner, by which means they are kept warm. Their food is raw beef or other coarse raw flesh."

PIGEONS AND PIGEON HOUSES

Pigeons were held of more importance than any other feathered stock, except in

---

* The English glead, gled, or kite has been extinct for many years.

those districts where goose-rearing was extensively carried on.

One important consideration in keeping pigeons was the original cost of the pigeon-house or cote, which, as usually built, required an outlay of from £100 to £150. The interior of the house made it costly, as many thousands of bricks were necessary in fitting shelves with divisions, so that each pair of birds had a separate box for nesting ; in this way the house would accommodate 100 to 200 pairs.

Pigeon-houses, on a much larger scale, built in early times, remain to show the importance attached by our ancestors to this stock.

The photograph facing this page is that of a double cote at Willington, in Bedfordshire, which was built in the time of Henry VIII (1509-1547).

I am also enabled to give an illustration of the interior of another old dovecote, at Ickwell Priory, in the same county ; this building is six-sided, and, making due allowance for the door, the walls provide nesting holes for about 570 pairs of birds.

There are several old dovecotes in my own neighbourhood ; all that I have seen are round buildings.

DOVECOTE AT WILLINGTON, BEDS.—TIME OF HENRY VIII

INTERIOR OF OLD DOVECOTE. ICKWELL PRIORY, BEDS.

Farmers were counselled to ignore the fancy breeds; the only two varieties that deserved their attention were the

"tame breed which lays and sits all the year round, and the common blue flight-breed, much less than the other, which breeds in seasons at seed-time and in harvest."

The latter were held preferable where a large number was kept.

The young pigeons commanded a ready sale, and the dung collected from the pigeon-house was worth 1s. 6d. a bushel. The birds may have done useful service by eating the seeds of injurious weeds, but the unfortunate farmer who had no pigeon-house found the necessary food on his land to feed birds belonging to his neighbours.

This was a real hardship in some districts, where one farmer who did not keep pigeons was surrounded on all sides by neighbours who kept large numbers of birds; but it was one of those evils for which the sufferer had no remedy.

The only thing the farmer could do was to begin pigeon-keeping himself, and find consolation in the thought that they obtained their share of his neighbours' crops.

Parkinson gives a curious account of the way a flight of pigeons which had deserted their cote was lured home again. He had built a cote at Cleethorpes, in Lincolnshire, and stocked it with four dozen young birds procured from a farmer about six miles away. Following the seller's advice, he kept them shut up and fed them well for 14 days and then gave them liberty. They remained about the place for a time and then disappeared.

Having been informed by a rat-catcher in the neighbourhood that he knew a method by which pigeons could be induced to return, Parkinson sent for him after the birds had been away about 14 days, an occasional one having been seen in the interval. The rat-catcher came and, having boiled some ingredients he brought with him, painted the pigeon-house carefully inside and out with the mixture. Parkinson expressing doubt as to the efficacy of the plan, the rat-catcher agreed to wait for his pay until the next day, when he maintained the birds would return, and if they did not return to claim no payment.

About eleven o'clock next morning one pigeon appeared and, after flying round and round at a great height as if fearful of alighting, settled on the cote, cooed, " repeatedly rubbed its nib where the ingredients had been applied, and at last flew away. About three o'clock the same day all my emigrants returned."

Parkinson supposed that the birds had been frightened away by the visit of an owl or cat, and, though he could not induce the rat-catcher to disclose the secret of the preparation with which he had painted the house, the smell led him to the conclusion that it contained assafœtida and salt.

Pigeons like the smell of the former and are excessively fond of the latter. The first arrival, carrying the smell of assafœtida on his plumage, might induce the others to return with him.

APPENDIX

KING GEORGE III

The great attention paid to the improvement of live-stock and to the betterment of agriculture which distinguished the period dealt with in the foregoing pages was very largely due to the close interest taken by King George III in all matters relating to the industry.

He took an active part in all schemes that promised to benefit agriculturists, and spared no pains to encourage and promote them. His patient, and ultimately successful, endeavour to break down the prejudice which existed against the Merino, alone entitles him to the affectionate nickname "Farmer George" bestowed on him by the country.

To the King's personal assistance may be traced the institution of the old Board of Agriculture and the institution of many of the Societies which were founded during his reign. Recognition of his influence is shown by the terms of a letter setting forth "Some Considerations on the Breed and Management of Horses" addressed to him in 1778, in which the following passage occurs : —

"The total neglect of all former regulations for the breed, the manifest degeneracy, the abuse and wanton destruction of horses, peculiar to modern times, are evils which affect the dearest interests of your Kingdom, the interests of population, of agriculture, and of commerce. From Your Majesty's paternal interference *only* can effectual reformation be expected."

In 1787, over the signature of "Ralph Robinson," he addressed to the *Annals of Agriculture* certain letters on husbandry in which he evinced a thorough knowledge of the management of various soils and exposed some leading errors in the then prevailing system of farming.

In 1791 the King sent a ram from his own lately imported flock of Merinos for the improvement of British wool in Scotland. The animal, which was selected with great care by the King himself, was declared to be the best specimen of the true Spanish breed that the Scottish Society had been able to obtain.

The King approved of selling, not giving away, his sheep. "Anyone may take a sheep, if given, and neglect it," said His Majesty, "but nobody will buy one who does not mean to take care of it." * Never-theless, as stated in the text, he did give away many in his endeavours to make the merits of Merinos better known.

Some of the finest sheep sent to Smithfield were his property.

Though the royal farms were not managed to the best advantage, the larger landed proprietors and others who had command of capital were eager to follow the King's example. The introduction of Merino sheep by the King had shown the capability and utility of the growth of fine wool, and the necessity and benefit of attending to our own native fine-woolled

* *George III : Court and Family*

breeds of sheep. The Duke of Bedford at Woburn, Mr. Coke at Holkham, and Mr. Curwen in Cumberland followed His Majesty's example.

In 1807 the Grand Junta presented him with a flock of Merinos numbering 2,000. The sheep, in pile and beauty, were the finest bred in Spain.

George III established three farms, each of a different soil and differently managed, at Windsor and Kew, and converted a portion of Richmond New Park into arable land; he also held, under his own management, the whole of the Old or Deer Park at Richmond, and farmed land at Mortlake, whereon he erected extensive farm buildings.

" The ground, like man," said the King, "was never meant to be idle ; if it does not produce something useful, it will be overrun with weeds." *

Windsor Great Park was not taken into cultivation until 1791, but in 1785 the Little Park was stocked with sheep and cattle, which shared it with the deer and hares. A thousand acres of the lightest part of the Great Park was converted into what is now known as the Norfolk Farm ; while 400 acres of good loamy soil formed the Flemish Farm. Though the remaining 2,400 acres were left in plantation and park, they were soon, from the improvements made on them, capable of carrying more stock than the whole had done before, and this without unnecessarily sacrificing a tree.

George III understood and loved horses, and was an excellent horseman and whip. When at Windsor, no matter what the weather, he generally rode the whole distance between that place and Buckingham Palace. He spent no little time in the royal stables.

* *Quarterly Review*

"Do you see that horse?" he once remarked to Lord
Winchelsea. "I have had him twenty years and he
is good now. Do you know the secret? I will tell it
you. I know his worth and treat him accordingly."*

George III's interest in agriculture increased until
the failure of his mental and bodily health. On
29th January, 1820, he died very quietly in his 82nd
year, and was buried at Windsor.

ROBERT BAKEWELL

Robert Bakewell, of The Grange, Dishley,
Loughborough, was born in 1726. He served his
apprenticeship to farming under his father, whom he
succeeded in 1773, but he took a prominent share in
the management of the farm for many years before his
father's death.

The farm at Dishley, in 1770, consisted of 440
acres, of which 110 were under the plough. The re-
mainder was given up to grass, the farm buildings, &c.
Bakewell was the first improver of grass-land in the
Kingdom by reason of his system of irrigation,
which enabled him to cut grass four times a year.
The stock on the farm averaged 60 horses, 400 sheep
and 150 cattle of all sorts and ages.

Visitors to Dishley were always impressed by
the scrupulous neatness, order and regularity that
prevailed, and by the ingenious devices for saving
labour.

Bakewell travelled much in England, seeking
information about farming methods in various

---

* *George III.* By B. Willson (1907)

districts and picking up useful hints concerning different breeds of stock. He also travelled abroad, and no doubt it was the neatness and cleanliness characteristic of the Dutch farms he visited that strengthened his love for orderly management at Dishley.

He maintained that intelligence and care in selection would enable the breeder to get beasts to weigh where you want them to weigh—in the roasting instead of the boiling pieces—and that the shape should give the greatest value in the smallest compass. He scouted the old notion that the blood must be constantly varied by mixing different breeds, and made it his principle to breed for small bone. His system was to breed within his own herd and flock, occasionally from closely related animals, and occasionally also from unrelated animals.

Bakewell's success, great as it was as a breeder of cattle, was principally in the production of the Dishley or New Leicester sheep.

Controversy raged for many years concerning the origin of the " Dishley sheep." Arthur Young and George Culley, who had better opportunities of ascertaining facts than others, agree that Lincoln blood was used, and Bakewell himself told Mr. Chaplin that at one time he had used " old Lincoln rams," by which we may understand Lincolns of the unimproved type.

Bakewell's enterprise did not cease with the production of the Dishley or New Leicester. He made further experiments and, by a judicious cross which he never divulged, produced yet another improvement. At his death he left two distinct types of sheep—the Dishley and another distinguished as the Improved or New Leicester, the former being renamed the " Dishley or Old Leicester."

One of the " sights " at Dishley was the museum, containing skeletons and pickled joints of the best sheep and cattle for comparison of one generation with the next.

Mention is made in the text (p. 45) of the fact that Bakewell originated the business of letting rams for the season. In 1760 he let out rams for a few shillings ; ten years later the fee for a season's use ranged up to 25 guineas, and within a few more years Bakewell's income from rams hired out was declared to amount to 3,000 guineas for a season. His famous ram Two Pounder was let for one season for 800 guineas in cash, and a reservation that one-third of the ewes covered should be Bakewell's own, which made the payment equivalent to 1,200 guineas.

He established, in 1783, the Dishley Society or Tup Club, in which he was moving spirit. The object of the club was to protect and advance the interests of breeders of improved stock.

Bakewell had no secrets about his horses. He used Dutch or Flemish blood to improve the old Black horses of Leicestershire. Others had the same opportunities, but it was reserved for him to turn them to the best account, and in 1785 he had the honour of showing a famous Black horse of his breeding to the King at St. James's. His horses were gentle and willing workers, slow but very powerful.

Of Bakewell's pigs little seems to have been recorded. Some have decided them as Berkshires, others as a mixed breed. What is known is that he inbred them very closely and made many experiments in fatting.

Probably no man in his position ever had the necessity for entertainment more forced upon him. Dishley was the show farm of England at a time when agriculture and stock-breeding were attracting a peculiarly wide measure of attention. In Bakewell's kitchen were entertained Russian princes, French and German royal dukes, British peers and sight-seers of every degree. As he practically kept open house for the countless visitors who came to Dishley, the task of entertaining them must have taxed his resources.

Robert Bakewell died, after a tedious illness, on 1st October, 1795. He bequeathed his flock and herd, which had never been dispersed, to his nephew, Mr. Honeybourn, who continued to breed at Dishley for some years.

GEORGE CULLEY

George Culley, born in 1735, devoted himself in early life to agriculture, especially to improving the breed of cattle. He was the earliest pupil of Robert Bakewell, and on leaving Dishley established himself with his brother in Northumberland, where the two did much to improve the local breeds of horses, cattle and sheep. Crowds visited the farm to see the results of their experiments.

Culley published many works on stock-raising and agriculture. He died at Fowberry Tower, Northumberland, on the 7th May, 1818.

THE DUKE OF BEDFORD

Francis Russell, 5th Duke of Bedford, was the son of Francis Russell, Marquis of Tavistock, who was killed by a fall from his horse on 22nd March, 1767. He succeeded his grandfather, John Russell, 4th Duke, in 1771. Devoted to politics in his early manhood, the principal employment of his later years was agriculture. He became a member of the original Board of Agriculture in 1793, and was first President of the Smithfield Club (17th December, 1798).

His model farm at Woburn was established with every convenience that could be desired for the breeding of cattle and experiments in farming. He made some valuable experiments upon the respective merits of the various breeds of sheep.* The Sheep-Shearings which he started at Woburn lasted for several days each year, and to these the whole agricultural world was invited. Ploughing and other competitions took place, wool and other products were sold, various exhibits were made, and prizes given.

The Duke died, unmarried, at Woburn, 2nd March, 1802, after an operation for strangulated hernia. He was buried at Chenies on 10th March, at night.

THE EARL OF EGREMONT

Sir George O'Brien Wyndham, 3rd Earl of Egremont, was born 18th December, 1751, and succeeded to the peerage at the age of twelve, on the

* _Annals of Agriculture_ (1795)

death of his father. He took little part in politics. In 1793 he was appointed to a seat on the Board of Agriculture. In addition to the Petworth estates and other property in England, he succeeded, in 1774, to the Irish property of his uncle, Percy Wyndham O'Brien, Earl of Thomond. For many years a leading figure in London society, he lived almost entirely at Petworth in his later years.

Lord Egremont made Petworth House a nursery of art and a college of agriculture. Arthur Young superintended the disafforesting of the great deer park. Lord Egremont was a most successful stock-breeder. He had a fine stud, and his horses won the Derby and Oaks oftener than those of any other owner.

It was as a patron of art that he was chiefly remarkable. He was a Vice-President of the British Institution, and was one of the first to appreciate Turner, who had a studio at Petworth. Charles Robert Leslie, Haydon, Constable and Flaxman were also frequently entertained and employed by him.

Egremont erected a market cross at Petworth, and built schools there. The road to Horsham was made under his directions. He died, unmarried, at Petworth on 11th November, 1837.

SIR JOHN SINCLAIR

Sir John Sinclair, first President of the old Board of Agriculture, was born 10th May, 1754, at Thurso Castle, Caithness. He inherited the extensive family estates in Caithness when only 16 years of age, and at once began improvements, one of which was the rapid construction of a road across the mountain of Cheilt, theretofore considered impassable.

In 1780 he became Member for Caithness. In 1782 he obtained a grant of £15,000 towards the relief of a serious famine in the North of Scotland. In 1784 Sinclair secured the seat for Lostwithiel, in Cornwall. In 1786 he made a tour through the north of Europe, visiting the courts of most of the Northern States, and being received in audience by the King of Sweden, Catherine of Russia, the King of Poland, and the Emperor Joseph.

In 1786 he was made a Baronet, with the almost unique privilege that the patent should include the male descendants of his daughter, should he die without an heir.

As President of a Special Committee of the Highland Society, Sinclair investigated the comparative merits of the wool of different breeds of sheep, especially of the Shetland flocks. He inaugurated the British Wool Society at a Sheep-Shearing festival in 1791 at Newhall's Inn, Queensferry.

He devoted much time and money to the improvement of his estates in Caithness. Land there was still cultivated on the " open-field " system, known in the Highlands as the " rig and rennel " method. He abolished the feudal services which still survived, and introduced an improved method of tillage founded on a regular rotation of crops and the cultivation of turnips, clover and rye-grass.

He improved the breeds of live-stock, encouraged sheep-farming, and introduced the Cheviot breed into Caithness. He planted trees, founded the herring-fishery at Wick, and established manufactures in Wick and Thurso.

10

He was largely instrumental in persuading Pitt to establish a Board of Agriculture, of which he was appointed President. The idea of a Board did not originate with Sir John, but his importunity forced the step on the Government.

In 1794 Sinclair raised a regiment of Fencibles, 600 strong, of which he was appointed Colonel. Subsequently he raised another regiment of 1,000 men, for service in Ireland.

His relations with Pitt becoming strained for a second time, at the annual election of the President of the Board of Agriculture, in 1798 Pitt set up in opposition Lord Somerville, who was elected by a majority of one. Sinclair's schemes had seriously embarrassed the Board during his five years' Presidency, and he left it in debt. In 1806 he resumed the office of President, and held it until 1813.

In 1810 he became a Member of the Privy Council, and a few months later received the appointment of Commissioner of Excise, a valuable sinecure. Acceptance of this office obliged him to resign his seat, after 30 years in the House. Two years later he retired from the Presidency of the Board of Agriculture, and withdrew into private life, residing chiefly in Edinburgh. He died 21st December, 1835. Sir John Sinclair married first, in 1776, Sarah, daughter of Alexander Maitland, who died in 1785, and, in 1788, Diana, daughter of Lord Macdonald, by whom he had a numerous family.

THOMAS COKE, EARL OF LEICESTER

Thomas William Coke, of Holkham, Earl of Leicester, was the eldest son of Robert Wenman, who took the name of Coke on succeeding to the estate of his maternal uncle, Thomas Coke. He was born 4th May, 1752.

He entered Parliament, very unwillingly, in 1776, as Member for Norfolk, in succession to his father, and sat until 1782. Re-elected in 1790, he held his seat till 1806. In 1807 he was elected for the Borough of Derby and afterwards again sat for Norfolk. He refused a peerage, but accepted it in 1837, when he was created Earl of Leicester and Viscount Coke.

In 1776, when he came into his estates, the whole district round Holkham was unenclosed and agriculture was at a very low ebb. The sheep were the old Norfolk breed, and, with the exception of a few milch cows, there were no cattle on the farms. The refusal of a tenant to accept renewal of his lease at a rent of five shillings an acre originated the improvements which made the estate famous. Coke determined to farm the land himself, but, being ignorant of farm management, he collected a number of practical men and entrusted the work to them. He made it an object-lesson, annually inviting the neighbouring farmers to examine the farm and discuss its management. These meetings gradually developed into the celebrated Holkham Sheep-Shearings, the last of which was held in 1821.

By an improved course of cropping, by the application of marl, not least by a change of live-stock, the land became so much improved that, in 1787, wheat was sown on it for the first time. The farmers were slow to follow Coke's example ; but at last he was able to boast truthfully that he had converted West Norfolk from a rye-growing to a wheat-producing district.

After experimenting with Dishley sheep and Merinos, Coke adopted Southdowns, which proved most suitable for the pasture.

With respect to cattle, he finally bred only Devons.

He greatly improved the Suffolk breed of pigs by crossing them with the Neapolitan, thereby obtaining superior meat.

It is said that the rental of his Holkham estate rose from £2,200, to above £20,000 under his management, the annual fall of timber and underwood averaging about £2,700. He spent over £100,000 on farmhouses and out-buildings.

On the death of the 5th Duke of Bedford, Coke became the chief agriculturist in the country.

Coke was a keen sportsman and one of the boldest riders and best shots in England. He married twice. He died at Longford Hall, Derbyshire, on 30th June, 1842, in his 91st year.

ARTHUR YOUNG

Arthur Young, son of the Rev. Arthur Young, Rector of Bradfield, Suffolk, was born at Whitehall on 11th September, 1741. In 1758 he left school at Lavenham and was apprenticed to Messrs. Robinson, of Lynn, with a view to entering Messrs. Tomlinson's counting-house. At Lynn he compiled political pamphlets, beginning in 1758 with *The Theatre of the present War in North America*, for which he received £10 in books. He also wrote four novels.

In 1759 his father died, much in debt, and Arthur Young left Lynn "without education, profession, or employment." The death of Mr. Tomlinson upset his scheme of a mercantile career, and, in 1761, he went to London, and started, at his own expense, and conducted for five months, a monthly magazine, *The Universal Museum*.

Returning to Bradfield, he took a farm of 80 acres, belonging to his mother, and farmed it from 1763 to 1766. In 1765 he married Martha Allen, of Lynn— an unhappy marriage from the outset. In 1766 he took a farm of 300 acres in Essex, tried experiments, lost money, and paid £100 to a farmer to take it off his hands. His successor is said to have made a fortune out of the place.

Having advertised for new farms, he made a tour of inspection of the places offered, and published his notes as *A Six Week's Tour through the Southern Counties of England and Wales* (1768). In this book, for the first time, the facts and principles of Norfolk husbandry were discussed in print. He then took a farm of 100 acres at North Mimms, Hertfordshire, which was, he says, not merely sterile land, but "hungry vitriolic gravel."

In 1769 he published *Letters concerning the Present State of the French Nation*, *Essay on the Management of Hogs*, and, in 1770, *The Expediency of a Free Importation of Corn at this Time*, which was warmly praised by the King.

His bookseller and his friends called for more tours. In 1770 appeared *A Six Months' Tour through the North of England*; in 1771, *The Farmer's Tour through*

the East of England, The Farmer's Calendar, of which
Dr. Paris mentions ten editions, and *Proposals for
Numbering the People*—a suggestion eventually adopted
in 1801.

In 1772 he published *Political Essays concerning the
Present State of the British Empire*. At this time his
circumstances were so straitened that he seriously
thought of going to America. In 1773 he undertook
to report the Parliamentary Debates for the *Morning
Post* at five guineas a week, walking home—17 miles—
to North Minns every Saturday and back on Monday.

In 1773 he wrote *Observations on the Present State of
the Waste-Lands of Great Britain*, and, in 1774,
Political Arithmetic. In 1776 he went to Ireland, but,
unfortunately, the journal of his tour, with specimens
of soils and minerals which he had collected, was
stolen from him.

From 1777 till 1779 he was Lord Kingsborough's
agent in Co. Cork; when he resigned the post he
again took a farm near his home. In 1780 he
published his *Tour in Ireland*, in which he attacked
the bounty on land carriage of corn to Dublin, with
the result that the bounty was reduced by half in
the next Session of Parliament.

In 1784 he commenced his celebrated *Annals of
Agriculture*. Forty-six volumes appeared continuously,
and among other contributors were George III (who
wrote under the name of his Windsor shepherd, Ralph
Robinson), Lord Orford, Mr. Coke of Holkham, and
Lord Bristol.

In 1785 Young's mother died and Bradfield became
his property. From May to November, 1787, he
toured in France. In 1788 he was deputed by the
wool growers of Suffolk to support a petition against

the Wool Bill, and was examined at the Bar of both Houses. He published two pamphlets on the subject, *The Question of Wool Truly Stated*.

In July, 1788, Young set out on his second French journey. After travelling 100 miles, his mare became blind, but he continued to ride her and returned to Bradfield in October, after an extended journey. He brought chicory seed from Lyons, and ultimately grew over 100 acres of it at Bradfield. In 1789 he made his last French journey, and in October, 1792, published his *Travels in France during the Years 1787, 1788 and 1789.*

In May, 1792, Young proposed "to arm the men of the Kingdom in a sort of Horse Militia." He himself joined a Yeomanry Corps at Bury.

Young now bought 4,400 acres of Yorkshire moor, but sold it almost immediately, on being appointed Secretary to the Board of Agriculture. He complained much of Sir John Sinclair, President of the Board, and of his appointment of incompetent persons to write the reports in several counties.

The death of his favourite daughter in 1797 greatly affected him. In 1811 he underwent an operation for cataract, but a week later news of the Duke of Grafton's death moved him to tears, and this destroyed all hope of recovering his sight.

He died at his official residence in Sackville Street on the 20th April, 1820, and was buried at Bradfield. His family became extinct on the death of his grandson in 1896.

LORD SOMERVILLE

John Southey, 15th Lord Somerville, was born at
Fitzhead Court, near Taunton, on 21st September,
1765. He succeeded to the title and estates on the
death of his father's elder brother in 1796; was
elected a representative Peer of Scotland in the House
of Lords, and was re-elected to the Parliaments of
1802 and 1806. In 1793 he was appointed an original
Member of the Board of Agriculture, and in 1798 was
elected its President. During his two years of office
he reduced the expenses of the Board within the
limit of the Parliamentary grant, and curbed the
extravagance which had involved it in difficulties.

Next to George III, who introduced Merino sheep
into England, he became the largest breeder and
owner of Merinos in the country. Two hundred of
his sheep sold for £10,000. In 1802 he visited Spain,
where he bought a valuable flock of pure Merinos;
during his stay he acquired a thorough knowledge of
the Spanish system of their management. He not
only devoted much time and attention to improving
sheep-breeding generally, but also invented several
useful agricultural implements.

In 1802 he started, in London, an annual show of
cattle, sheep, and pigs, &c., for which he provided the
prizes. He was a constant attendant at the Sheep-
Sheerings at Holkham and Woburn.

He died of dysentery at Vevay, in Switzerland,
on the 5th October, 1819. He was buried at Aston-
Somerville.

SIR JOSEPH BANKS

Sir Joseph Banks was born on the 13th February, 1743(4). His father died in 1761, leaving him an ample fortune and estate at Revesby, Lincolnshire.

In May, 1766, Banks was elected a Fellow of the Royal Society, and during that summer went to Newfoundland to make a collection of plants. After his return he made the acquaintance of Dr. Daniel Solander, a favourite pupil of Linnæus and an Assistant Librarian at the British Museum. Solander was his companion on his tour round the world, and later became his Librarian.

Banks accompanied Cook's expedition in the "Endeavour," which, leaving England in August, 1768, visited South America, Tahiti, New Zealand, Australia, New Guinea, Batavia, the Cape of Good Hope and St. Helena, and reached England again in June, 1771.

In November, 1778, he became President of the Royal Society, and held the position until his death. His determination to reform certain abuses led to some discontent, and a few members left the Society. In 1802 he was chosen a member of the National Institute of France. He died at Isleworth on the 19th June, 1820.

The writings of Sir Joseph Banks are comparatively insignificant. On the death of Dr. Solander he seems to have given up all idea of publishing the account of his travels and collections. The MSS. are preserved in the Botanical Department of the British Museum.

WILLIAM MARSHALL

William Marshall was baptised on 28th July, 1745, at Sinnington, Yorkshire. In 1774 he undertook the management of a 300 acre farm near Croydon, where, in 1778, he wrote his first work, *Minutes of Agriculture made on a Farm of 300 Acres of Various Soils, near Croydon.* In 1779 he published *Experiments and Observations concerning Agriculture and the Weather.* In 1780 he was appointed agent on the Norfolk estate of Sir Harbord Harbord. In 1783 he contributed to the *Philosophical Transactions* an account of the "Black Canker Caterpillar which destroys the Turnips in Norfolk." He left Norfolk in 1784 and settled at Stafford.

His *Arboretum Americanum,* an alphabetical catalogue of American Forest Trees and Shrubs, appeared in 1785. From 1786 to 1808 he lived in Clement's Inn, London, during the winter, travelling in the country during the summer.

His chief publication was *A General Survey, from Personal Experience, Observation, and Enquiry, of the Rural Economy of England.* In his *Rural Economy of the Midland Counties* he proposed the establishment of a Board of Agriculture. His proposal received effect in 1793.

In 1808 he bought a large estate in his native place, Cleveland, Yorkshire, and retired thither. His latter years were devoted to compiling *A Review and Complete Abstract of the Reports of the Board of Agriculture on the Several Counties of England.* In 1779 he published *Proposals for a Rural Institute or College of Agriculture,* and was building such an institute at Pickering when he died, on 18th September, 1818.